THE POETICAL BOOKS

D1370532

Set 4

THE
POETICAL
BOOKS

JOB, PSALMS, PROVERBS,
ECCLESIASTES, AND SONG OF SOLOMON

SET 4

BIG
DREAM
MINISTRIES

No part of *The Amazing Collection*, whether audio, video, or print, may be reproduced in any form without written permission from Big Dream Ministries, Inc., P.O. Box 324, 12460 Crabapple Road, Suite 202, Alpharetta, Georgia 30004. 1-678-366-3460
www.theamazingcollection.org

ISBN-13: 978-1-932199-04-8
ISBN-10: 1-932199-04-7

Cover design by Brand Navigation and Arvid Wallen
Cover composite image by Getty Images and Corbis
Creative Team: Leigh McLeroy, Kathy Mosier, Pat Reinheimer, Glynese Northam

Some of the anecdotal illustrations in this book are true to life and are included with the permission of the persons involved. All other illustrations are composites of real situations, and any resemblance to people living or dead is coincidental.

All Scripture quotations in this publication are taken from the *New American Standard Bible* (NASB), © The Lockman Foundation 1960, 1962, 1963, 1968, 1971, 1972, 1973, 1975, 1977, 1995.

Printed in the United States

7 8 9 10 / 16 15 14

Welcome to
The Amazing Collection
The Bible, Book by Book

It is amazing how a love letter arriving at just the right time can gladden the heart, refresh the soul, and restore the passion of the beloved. When lovers are separated by distance and can communicate only through the written word, that word becomes the lifeline of their love.

The greatest love letter ever written often sits on our shelves unopened as we go about our lives, sometimes fearful, burdened, anxious, in pain, and in doubt, not knowing that on its pages we can find all we need to live the life we have always wanted.

In this love letter we will discover God, and through Him we will receive hope, assurance, freedom from fear, guidance for everyday life, wisdom, joy, peace, power, and above all, the way to salvation. We will find the life we have always longed for — *abundant* life.

The Bible is simply a love letter compiled into sixty-six books and written over a period of sixteen hundred years by more than forty authors living on three continents. Although the authors came from different backgrounds, there is one message, one theme, one thread that runs throughout the entire Bible from the first book, Genesis, to the last book, Revelation. That message is God's redeeming love for mankind — a message that is as relevant for us today as it was two thousand years ago.

God has written the Bible so that men and women might enter into an intimate relationship with Him and see His character, His works, His power, and His love. It would be tragic to read these books and never come to know your God! Therefore, as you go through this study, listen to the lectures, read the Scripture, and do your daily homework. Make it your heart's desire to know God intimately. Read each page of the Bible as if it were a love letter written by the hand of God to you personally. Bask in His great love, stand in awe of His mighty power, bow before His majesty, and give thanksgiving and adoration to the One who is all-present, all-knowing, all-merciful, and all-loving. He is on every page, and He is speaking to you.

The Bible is a book inspired by God Himself. It is His story, His love letter, His invitation to you to become His child through His Son, Jesus Christ. It is the Word of God . . . indeed, the most Amazing Collection.

CONTENTS

Table of Maps, Charts, and Diagrams   10

Workbook Guide   11

Overview of The Poetical Books   14

Introduction to The Poetical Books   19

JOB

Introduction   23

Overview   25

Learning for Life   27

Day One: The Big Picture   28

Day Two: A Prominent Player   31

Day Three: A Crucial Chapter   34

Day Four: A Notable Feature   37

Day Five: A Timeless Principle   40

Review   43

PSALMS

Introduction   47

Overview   49

Learning for Life   51

Day One: The Big Picture 52

Day Two: A Crucial Chapter 55

Day Three: A Prominent Player 58

Day Four: A Notable Feature 61

Day Five: A Timeless Principle 64

Review 67

PROVERBS

Introduction 71

Overview 73

Learning for Life 76

Day One: The Big Picture 77

Day Two: A Crucial Chapter 80

Day Three: A Prominent Player 83

Day Four: A Notable Feature 86

Day Five: A Timeless Principle 89

Review 92

ECCLESIASTES

Introduction 95

Overview 97

Learning for Life 99

Day One: The Big Picture 100

Day Two: A Crucial Chapter 103

Day Three: A Notable Feature 106

Day Four: A Prominent Player 109

Day Five: A Timeless Principle 112

Review 115

SONG OF SOLOMON

Introduction 119

Overview 121

Learning for Life 124

Day One: The Big Picture 125

Day Two: Notable Feature Number 1 128

Day Three: Notable Feature Number 2 131

Day Four: Notable Feature Number 3 134

Day Five: A Timeless Principle 137

Review 140

Comprehensive Review of The Poetical Books 141

Congratulations! 144

Answer Key to Outlines 146

Notes 153

Biographies 155

Leader's Guide 159

MAPS, CHARTS, AND DIAGRAMS

The Poetical Books at a Glance   13

JOB

    Map   24

    The Controversies in Job   29

    Arguments of Job's Friends   29

PSALMS

    The Five Books of Psalms   53

    Types of Psalms   54

    Hebrew Parallelism   55

PROVERBS

    Divisions of Proverbs   78

    Proverbs: A Hinge Book   80

    Characters in Proverbs   82

ECCLESIASTES

    Ecclesiastes at a Glance   101

SONG OF SOLOMON

    Love in the Song of Solomon   127

Chronological Relationship of the Old Testament Books   145

WORKBOOK GUIDE

The Amazing Collection is a study of the Bible, book by book. This fourth study includes the five books of the Bible referred to as The Poetical Books. The following will acquaint you with the design of this series.

The entire Bible will be studied one book at a time through a teaching video and a written study. The teaching video includes music to stir the heart, graphics to enlighten the mind, and a personal testimony to bring the theme of that particular book to life.

The workbook contains:

1. An introduction to summarize each book.

2. Outlines to be used while watching each of the teaching videos. The answers to the outline blanks are given during the videos and can also be found in the key at the back of your workbook.

3. *Learning for Life* discussion questions to be used after viewing the videos. (If your group is large, we recommend forming small discussion groups.)

4. Five daily lessons of homework for each book.

5. A memory verse for each book.

6. Various maps, charts, and diagrams.

7. A review at the end of each book to refresh your memory. The answers to the review are found in the *Review It!* sections in the margins at the end of the lessons for Day One through Day Four. The fifth review question is a review of the memory verse.

Before you begin the homework, ask God to show you how to apply the truths of Scripture to your own life. At the beginning of each day's lesson in the workbook, there are two choices for the daily reading. The *Complete Read* enables you to read the entire book over the course of that study. During busy times, the *Quick Read* allows you to read a few key chapters or verses from that book. The daily lesson will require a small amount of time each day to complete. Of course, feel free to extend that time with additional study.

One of the incredible things about the Word of God is that you can read the same Scripture at different times in your life and gain new insights with each reading. God's Word is inexhaustible, and it is living; it has the power to produce life-changing results.

Our prayer for you as you journey through *The Amazing Collection* is that you will learn for life the purpose, main characters, geography, and time period of every book in the Bible. But above all, we pray that you will come to know more intimately the God of the Bible, His Son Jesus Christ, and the Holy Spirit.

THE POETICAL BOOKS AT A GLANCE

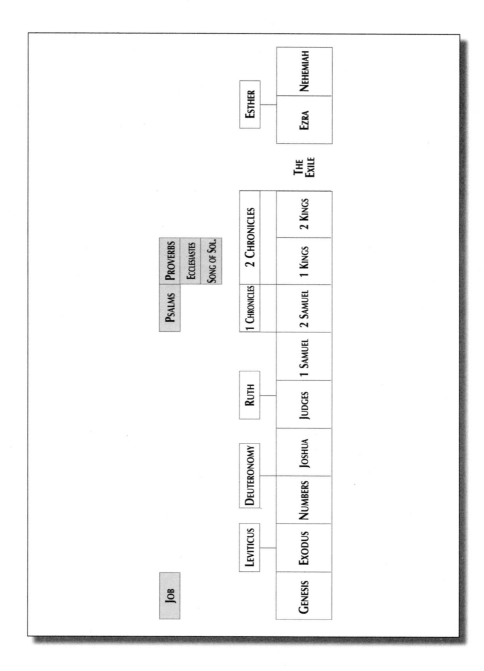

To see how these books fit into the chronology of the Old Testament books as a whole, see the chart on page 145.

OVERVIEW OF THE POETICAL BOOKS

The following pages provide an overview of each of the books you will be studying in this set. They are designed to be cut out and used as quick reference cards with the main facts of the book on the front and the memory verse on the back.

You might find it helpful to laminate them and carry them with you on a ring or keep them in a card holder in a place where you'll be able to refer to them often.

It is our hope that this will be a tool that will help you truly learn these books for life.

JOB
Sovereignty of God

WHO:
Job
Job's Three Friends

WHAT:
Man's Suffering
God's Sovereignty

WHERE:
Uz

Time Period: 2000 BC

PSALMS
Life of Worship

WHO:
David
Sons of Korah
Asaph
Solomon
Heman
Ethan
Moses

WHAT:
Collection of Hymns

WHERE:
Israel

Span of Authors: 1,000 Years

PROVERBS
Life of Wisdom

WHO:
Solomon

WHAT:
Practical Instruction
for Wise Living

WHERE:
Israel/Judah

Time Written: 950–700 BC

JOB
Sovereignty of God

Naked I came from my mother's womb,
And naked I shall return there.
The LORD gave and the LORD has taken away.
Blessed be the name of the LORD.

JOB 1:21

PSALMS
Life of Worship

One thing I have asked from the LORD, that I shall seek:
That I may dwell in the house of the LORD all the days of my life,
To behold the beauty of the LORD
And to meditate in His temple.

PSALM 27:4

PROVERBS
Life of Wisdom

The fear of the LORD is the beginning of wisdom,
And the knowledge of the Holy One is understanding.

PROVERBS 9:10

ECCLESIASTES
Life of Enjoyment

WHO:
Solomon

WHAT:
A Philosophical View
of Life

WHERE:
"Under the Sun"

Time Period: About 935 BC

SONG OF SOLOMON
Marriage of Intimacy

WHO:
Solomon
The Shulammite

WHAT:
Exalts Love and
Sexuality
in Marriage

WHERE:
Israel

Time Period: About 965 BC

ECCLESIASTES
Life of Enjoyment

The conclusion, when all has been heard, is: fear God and keep His commandments, because this applies to every person.

ECCLESIASTES 12:13

SONG OF SOLOMON
Marriage of Intimacy

Many waters cannot quench love,
Nor will rivers overflow it;
If a man were to give all the riches of his house for love,
It would be utterly despised.

SONG OF SOLOMON 8:7

INTRODUCTION TO THE POETICAL BOOKS

The Poetical Books reveal the heart of the nation of Israel and are considered some of the finest literature ever written. It is as if the authors' very hearts have been opened up for all to see. Pain is not minimized, nor is man's struggle to understand God downplayed. Questions of suffering are boldly asked, worship is gloriously displayed, wisdom is held in highest esteem, married sexual love is unashamedly portrayed, and philosophy is openly debated.

Hebrew poetry is not structured around the rhyme or meter we are used to reading and hearing. Instead, ideas are often stated in one line and then reinforced in the second line, or a second line is composed to add to or complete the thoughts of the first. In other forms, the second line of poetry contrasts the first.

Job and Song of Solomon were written as dramatic poems that tell a story. Most of the psalms were written to be accompanied by an instrument and are thus examples of lyric poetry — rich in its language of worship and praise. Proverbs and Ecclesiastes are examples of didactic poetry, giving instructions or lessons about life in short concise verses.

As we study these poetical books, you will be amazed at their beauty, clarity, and passion. At times it may seem that their writers have been reading your diary! As they reveal *their* hearts, we find they are much like our own.

So as we continue this great adventure with God, drink in the beauty and blessing, the comfort and the joy of these lovely books inspired by the very heart and Spirit of God.

JOB

[Sovereignty of God]

Naked I came from my mother's womb,

And naked I shall return there.

The LORD gave and the LORD has taken away.

Blessed be the name of the LORD.

JOB 1:21

JOB
[Sovereignty of God]

INTRODUCTION

The life of peace and pleasure that was offered Adam and Eve in the Garden of Eden was forever interrupted by pain and suffering after the Fall. Disease, war, deceit, infertility, loss of property, and the death of loved ones fill the pages of recorded human history.

Where is God during these times of trial and trouble, and how should we respond to them? These questions have long been asked, and few answers can be found that satisfy the heart of man. Job was a man who lived during the times of the patriarchs, and his early life was marked by peace and prosperity. But when tragedy struck, Job's world rapidly unraveled. As the book bearing his name opens, we find a drama taking place in heaven that rivals the one in Job's earthly life.

Though God remained silent during much of Job's suffering, his friends did not. They came on the scene to offer comfort but soon became accusers as they questioned the cause of Job's suffering. At the end of the book, God provided His answer. It was not the one Job wanted, nor is it the answer we seek. Behind the scenes of our suffering, an all-powerful, all-loving, and faithful God asks us to trust Him. He is God . . . and He is in control.

This exquisite dramatic poem is considered one of the finest pieces of literature ever written. For four thousand years it has brought comfort, hope, and encouragement to those who wrestle with the question of man's suffering and God's sovereignty.

JOB
[Sovereignty of God]

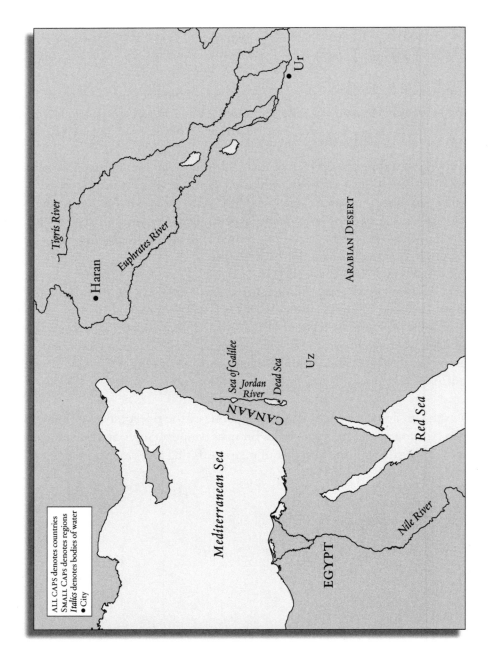

JOB
[Sovereignty of God]

OVERVIEW

WHO: Author: Unknown
Main Character: Job

WHAT: A narrative poem

WHEN: Events in the book take place around the time of Abraham (2000 BC)

WHERE: Uz, located southeast of the Dead Sea in the area of Edom

WHY: The theme is the suffering of man and the sovereignty of God

I. CONTROVERSY: IN HEAVEN BETWEEN GOD AND SATAN

A. God's wager before Satan: "Have you considered my servant ___Job___ ?"

  1. Satan argued that Job was righteous because God gave him _everything_

  2. Satan was given permission to take away Job's wealth.

    a. Satan took away all of Job's _possessions_ .

    b. Satan took away Job's _children_ .

  3. Job's response: "Naked I came from my mother's womb,
               And naked I shall return there.
               The LORD gave and the LORD has taken away.
               Blessed be the name of the LORD." (Job 1:21)

  4. Satan was given permission to take away Job's health.

    a. Job was covered with _boils_ from head to foot.

    b. He suffered severe depression.

II. CONTROVERSY: ON EARTH BETWEEN JOB AND HIS FRIENDS

A. Friends came to comfort Job because of his suffering.

  1. They _weep_ over the suffering of Job.

2. They sat in silence for _____seven_____ days.

B. Friends confronted Job that his suffering must be because he had sinned.

1. Eliphaz argued from _____experience_____.

2. Bildad argued from _____tradition_____.

3. Zophar argued from _____common sense_____.

a. First cycle was general: mild _____suggestion_____.

b. Second cycle was specific: _____condemnation_____.

c. Third cycle was very specific: _____harsh_____ reproof.

C. Job became more_____self_____ focused (Job 29).

D. Job called God into the _____courtroom_____ (Job 23:3-7).

E. Elihu, the youngest, argued from _____wisdom_____.

III. CONTROVERSY: ON EARTH BETWEEN GOD AND JOB

A. God spoke to Job from a _____whirlwind_____ (Job 38).

B. Through a series of questions God revealed His _____wisdom_____.

1. Job acknowledged his insignificance.

2. Job responded with _____silence_____.

C. God revealed His _____power_____.

1. Job acknowledged God's sovereignty.

2. Job _____repented_____.

D. God blessed Job with twice as many possessions.

APPLICATION

The suffering of Job is shrouded in the sovereignty of God.

JOB
[Sovereignty of God]

LEARNING FOR LIFE

1. Review: Give an overview of The Kingdom Books from Joshua through Nehemiah (group effort).

2. How do The Poetical Books differ from The Kingdom Books?

3. If you had been Job's friend, what might your response have been to his suffering?

4. How do you respond to suffering when it enters your life? Give an example.

5. How does God want His children to respond to suffering?

6. How can the questions God asks Job help us in our time of trials?

JOB
[Sovereignty of God]

INTERESTING!
Of John Calvin's 700
sermons, 159 centered
around the book of Job.

DAY ONE

COMPLETE READ: Chapters 1–8
QUICK READ: Chapters 1–2

THE BIG PICTURE

> I call this book . . . one of the grandest things ever written with pen. There is nothing written . . . in the Bible or out of it, of equal literary merit.
>
> —THOMAS CARLYLE

> The greatest poem, whether of ancient or modern literature.
>
> —ALFRED LORD TENNYSON

> More magnificent and sublime than any other book of scripture.
>
> —MARTIN LUTHER

> Perhaps the greatest masterpiece of the human mind.
>
> —VICTOR HUGO

A Christian is someone who shares the suffering of God in the world.
—DIETRICH BONHOEFFER, German theologian executed during World War II

Can you imagine accolades more impressive than these? Words such as *grandest*, *greatest*, *magnificent*, and *sublime* are undoubtedly appropriate. But for most of us, studying the book of Job is anything but a grand experience. The book of Job can seem long, confusing, and obscure. We know he suffers and is taunted for his patience. We know friends give him advice but only make things worse. And we know that everything ultimately ends well. But beyond that, we can feel overwhelmed by the book's challenging content. Let's look at the Big Picture of Job and see if it helps our understanding.

Job lived long ago, most likely during the time of Abraham around 2000 BC. Opinions differ on exact timing, but factors in the book — family sacrifices, Job's longevity, assets of cattle and possessions rather than money, and characters that are nomadic rather than city-dwelling — all point to the time of Abraham.

We have no way of knowing with certainty who wrote the book. Various scholars have suggested Job, Moses, Solomon, Isaiah, and Ezra, but there's not enough definitive proof to be sure.

As the chart that follows indicates, the book of Job revolves around controversy.

Controversy Between God and Satan	Controversy Between Job and His friends	Controversy Between God and Job
1 3	4 37	38 42

In chapters 1–3, Satan challenged God about Job's righteousness, charging that Job served God only because God protected and blessed him. God gave Satan permission to test Job to prove his sincerity, and he came through with flying colors. God prevailed.

The most confusing section of the book is chapters 4–37. In these chapters, Job's friends argued that his troubles had come because of sin. Job refuted their theory and counterargued that he had done nothing wrong. No one prevailed. The following chart, incorporating ideas of Dr. Roy B. Zuck, will help you sense

ARGUMENTS OF JOB'S FRIENDS		
ROUND ONE	ROUND TWO	ROUND THREE
God Punishes the Wicked and Blesses the Good	*The Wicked Suffer and Perish*	*God Is Majestic and You Are Wicked*
4 14	15 21	22 37
General	Specific	Very Specific

Enter my present trouble, God of strength and compassion. Protect me from despair and from faintheartedness. Encourage me with hope. Make me strong in Christ, "the One at Your right hand."
—EUGENE PETERSON, pastor and author

the overall thrust of the arguments presented by Job's friends.

In the third section, chapters 38–42, God challenged Job. In an eloquent and often fiery speech, God described the details of His creation, contrasting His own omniscience and sovereignty with Job's incontestable dependency and smallness. And God prevailed again. Job's testimony of submission is in 42:5-6:

> I have heard of You by the hearing of the ear;
> But now my eye sees You;
> Therefore I retract,
> And I repent in dust and ashes.

From the human perspective, the theme of Job is the suffering of man and the questions surrounding it. But from the divine perspective, the theme is the sovereignty of God and its relationship to human suffering.

Job repeatedly asked, "Why am I suffering?" but he never got an answer. Instead, God opened Job's eyes to see His glory and His power. By the end of the book, Job's need for an answer had evaporated.

What thoughts and feelings (either encouraging or unsettling) do you have when you meditate on the sovereignty of God?

unsettling

MEMORY VERSE

> Naked I came from my mother's womb,
> And naked I shall return there.
> The LORD gave and the LORD has taken away.
> Blessed be the name of the LORD.
>
> JOB 1:21

JOB
[Sovereignty of God]

DAY TWO

FACT
Job is cited as a
positive role model in
James 5:11.

COMPLETE READ: Chapters 9–17
QUICK READ: Passages in this day's lesson

A PROMINENT PLAYER

Besides God, who else could qualify as our Prominent Player in this book? Only Job. Yet don't you think Job desperately wished to be excused from his part in the play? When we first meet Job, he was quietly living a godly, peaceful life. But in three quick strikes like lightning bolts from heaven, he lost everything. The first strike destroyed his worldly goods — oxen, donkeys, sheep, camels, and servants. The second strike killed *all ten* of his children. The third strike smote his own body with open running sores, a fever, and foul breath — no one wanted to come near him. His home became the city dump.

Job didn't have a clue why his life had been turned upside down. It would be easy to underestimate the confusion, darkness, and horror he must have suffered — because we know the end of the story and what was going on behind the scenes. In 1:6-12 and 2:1-6, the reader is privy to events that Job knew nothing about.

Summarize what took place in those two scenes.

God + Satan

Philip Yancey writes,

I have sat now with something broken inside me for months, and the words — death, grief, fear — don't touch my wounds.
—CHARLES BOWDEN, author

> The view behind the curtain in chapters 1–2 reveals that Job was being exalted, not spurned. God was letting his

JUST A THOUGHT
Job's wife probably
could have been a bit
more helpful!

own reputation ride on the response of a single human being. At the time when Job felt most abandoned, at that very time God was giving him personal, almost microscopic scrutiny. God seemed absent; in one sense God had never been more present.[1]

Living out the test, but totally ignorant of the divine stakes involved, Job's response to these devastating events was a shining example of endurance, faithfulness, and trust. Briefly describe his response as recorded in chapters 1 and 2.

Fell to the ground to worship still kept his trust in God

Once Job's friends arrived and tried to comfort him, his response began to change. As time drug on, he started complaining and angrily venting. He started asking, "Why?" and eventually demanded an explanation from God. Read the following verses and briefly describe the emotions you see in Job.

3:11-13
Why was I even born

God does not keep [us] from trouble; He says — "I will be with [you] in trouble." Tribulation is never a noble thing; but let tribulation be what it may — exhausting, galling, frustrating, it is not able to separate us from the love of God.

—Oswald Chambers, *My Utmost for His Highest*

6:8-10
God to take his life

7:19-20
Questioning why

9:16-18
Not sure if it would help to ~~talk to~~ God personally

10:1-7
self pity loathes his life

16:9
Object of Gods wrath

19:6-11
Torn down by God

30:20-21
pleads c God

32

How do you feel about Job's honesty with God?

Interestingly, God never seemed to take Job to task for speaking so honestly and harshly. God's problem with Job was not his anger; it was his perspective. Job's view of God was much too small. And that's the issue God addressed toward the end of the book. Read the verses below and jot down words that describe Job at this point.

40:3-5 *Shut up and listen*

42:1-6
    Repentance

You've read and thought about Job's verbal responses at different stages of his ordeal. Write a brief description of him as you presently understand him.

grieving   anger
self pity   repent.
self loathing

Chapters 1 and 2 make plain how much was at stake in Job's test and response. And it is always that way — even for us. C. S. Lewis writes, "There is no neutral ground in the universe: every square inch, every split second, is claimed by God and counterclaimed by Satan."[2]

Respond in prayer to this statement.

MEMORY VERSE

Naked I came from my mother's womb,
And naked I shall return there.
The LORD gave and the LORD has taken away.
Blessed be the name of the LORD.

JOB 1:21

> *Nothing that grieves us can be called little: by the eternal laws of proportion a child's loss of a doll and a king's loss of a crown are events of the same size.*
> —MARK TWAIN, author and humorist

REVIEW IT!
The Prominent Player in the book is Job.

JOB
[Sovereignty of God]

DAY THREE

COMPLETE READ: Chapters 18–25
QUICK READ: Chapter 42

A CRUCIAL CHAPTER

> If knowing answers to life's questions is absolutely necessary to you, then forget the journey. You will never make it, for this is a journey of unknowables — of unanswered questions, enigmas, incomprehensibles, and most of all, things unfair.
>
> —MADAME JEANNE GUYON

If ever there was a man who wanted answers to life's questions, it was Job. Along his journey, he desperately tried to solve enigmas, grasp incomprehensible events, and right things that were unfair. But his best efforts failed. Near the end of his story, Job came to understand and embrace the truth that God's ways are unsearchable — and out of the soil of despair and failure, growth, maturity, and blessing sprang forth.

Chapter 42 records Job's hard-won growth. You looked briefly at verses 1–6 of this chapter on Day Two. Now take a closer and more comprehensive look at this Crucial Chapter. Read verses 1 and 2 and describe in your own words what Job was affirming.

God can do ALL things for his own purpose and it was not for Job to understand

Faith sees the divine action in everything; faith believes that Jesus Christ is alive in everything. Could we pierce the veil, and were we vigilant and attentive, God would reveal Himself continuously to us and we would rejoice in His action in everything that happened to us. At every occurrence we would say: Dominus est — it is the Lord.

—JEAN-PIERRE DE CAUSSADE, eighteenth-century Jesuit priest

What was Job saying about himself in verses 3 and 4?

That he did not understand + he decided to sit back and listen

In verse 5, Job indicated that he previously had lived with one level of understanding of God but as a result of his trials had been taken to an entirely different level. Not only had he seen more deeply into God's character, but he also had seen more deeply into himself and the circumstances of life. His response to this understanding was to retract his words and repent in dust and ashes. From what do you think Job felt he needed to repent?

loss of faith and trust

Beginning with verse 7, it becomes clear that God was not only on Job's side, but also very pleased with him. Read verses 7-17 and record the phrases that indicate God's pleasure with Job.

*Job spoke the truth about God
Job will pray for his friends + God will forgive them
Gave him twice as much by blessing his latter part of life*

In these verses, God's blessings for Job are very tangible. How would you feel about the conclusion of this story if it had ended after verse 9 rather than continuing through verse 17?

That Gods favor and blessing would be enough

When pain is to be borne, a little courage helps more than much knowledge, a little human sympathy more than much courage, and the least tincture of the love of God more than all.

—C. S. Lewis, author, professor, and theologian

After we endure a great ordeal, should God always be expected to bless us as He did Job in verses 10-17? Why or why not?

Hopefully, maybe not necessarily by 'material' blessing but God blessing

To our wounds only thy wounds can speak, and no God has wounds but thou alone.

—EDWARD SHILLITO, pastor and poet

It's interesting to note that God doubled the amount of worldly goods He had allowed Satan to take from Job (compare 1:3 and 42:12). But only the *same* number of children he had lost were born to him again. God knew Job's pain at the loss of his children could not be soothed in this life simply by doubling their number. Yet, in heaven and for all eternity, Job enjoys the blessing and reunion of all his children — twofold.

As you reflect on Job's story, consider the relevance of Psalm 115:3:

> But our God is in the heavens;
> He does whatever He pleases.

REVIEW IT!
Chapter 42 is our Crucial Chapter because Job repented and God blessed him.

MEMORY VERSE

Naked I came from my mother's womb,
And naked I shall return there.
The LORD gave and the LORD has taken away.
Blessed be the name of the LORD.

JOB 1:21

JOB
[Sovereignty of God]

DAY FOUR

COMPLETE READ: Chapters 26–37
QUICK READ: Chapter 38

FACT
The dunghill was used in ancient cities to provide fuel. Dried dung was cut up and burned.

A NOTABLE FEATURE

On January 7, 1855, the minister of New Park Street Chapel, Southward, opened his morning sermon with these words:

> It has been said by someone that "the proper study of mankind is man." I will not oppose the idea, but I believe it is equally true that the proper study of God's elect is God; the proper study of a Christian is the Godhead. The highest science, the loftiest speculation, the mightiest philosophy, which can ever engage the attention of a child of God, is the name, the nature, the person, the work, the doings, and the existence of the great God whom he calls his Father.
>
> There is something exceedingly improving to the mind in a contemplation of the divinity. It is a subject so vast, that all our thoughts are lost in its immensity; so deep, that our pride is drowned in its infinity. Other subjects we can compass and grapple with; in them we feel a kind of self-content and go our way with the thought, 'Behold I am wise.' But when we come to this master-science, finding that our plumb line cannot sound its depth, and that our eagle eye cannot see its height, we turn away with the thought that vain man would be wise, but he is like a wild ass's colt; and with solemn exclamation, "I am but of yesterday, and know nothing." No subject of contemplation will tend more to humble the mind, than thoughts of God.[3]

Never despair of the mercy of God.
—SAINT BENEDICT, *The Rule of Benedict*

DID YOU KNOW?
Job's righteousness is
mentioned twice in the
book of Ezekiel
(14:14,20).

These words were spoken a century and a half ago by C. H. Spurgeon — when he was only twenty years old! What marvelous words, then and now. And what marvelous motivation to explore chapters 38–41 of the book of Job. There may not be another passage in the entire Bible that so tenaciously explores the power and the knowledge and the presence of God. This Notable Feature takes on even more potency in these chapters because the words come directly from the mouth of God to Job. And as Spurgeon said, the words are "so vast, that all our thoughts are lost in its immensity; so deep, that our pride is drowned in its infinity."

God had listened patiently to Job and his friends. And now the time had come for Him to speak — and for Job to listen. His words are eloquently poignant and their message profound. God asked question after question of Job, each one increasing the chasm between who God is and who Job is — until seeing from one side of the chasm to the other was impossible. God began this life-changing encounter with Job in 38:1-3:

> Then the LORD answered Job out of the whirlwind and said,
> "Who is this that darkens counsel
> By words without knowledge?
> "Now gird up your loins like a man
> And I will ask you, and you instruct Me!"

In other words, "Who is this who doesn't know what he's talking about? I've got some questions I need you to answer for Me." As you read the following verses, write down what you think God was trying to teach Job about God's identity and about his own?

38:4-5 *who built the earth*

38:12 *who is boss*

38:16-18 *Have you been every where*

*Wouldn't they find it a
source of consolation
to see that light and
darkness, hope and
despair, love and fear
are never very far from
each other, that
spiritual freedom often
requires a fierce
spiritual battle?*

—HENRI NOUWEN,
twentieth-century priest
and author

38:19 *who created light & dark*

38:28-29 *who created rain & ice the changing seasons*

38:30-32 *who created the mountains & stars*

38:41 *provides food for the birds*

39:26-27 *created the birds to fly*

40:7-9 *provides justice*

41:11 *who owns everything*

How do you think Job felt once God completed the litany of His incomparable abilities? List some words that might describe his emotional state.

humbled
ashamed

In *The Knowledge of the Holy*, A. W. Tozer writes, "What comes into our minds when we think about God is the most important thing about us."[4] Admittedly, these chapters open only small windows into the great vista that is God. But based on them, what comes into your mind when you think about God?

What help could that be for your next trial?

I am not in control

MEMORY VERSE

Naked I came from my mother's womb,
And naked I shall return there.
The LORD gave and the LORD has taken away.
Blessed be the name of the LORD.

JOB 1:21

O, God, within the sometimes puzzling experiences of this pilgrimage, I will gratefully sing of Your steadfast love and Your faithfulness which, despite my stuttering steps and recurrent doubt, steadily develop a redeeming purpose in my life.

—EUGENE PETERSON, pastor and author

REVIEW IT!
Our Notable Feature is the book's description of God's sovereignty over all creation.

JOB
[Sovereignty of God]

DAY FIVE

COMPLETE READ: Chapters 38—42
QUICK READ: Chapters 40—42

A TIMELESS PRINCIPLE

> We cannot understand the meaning of man's trials; God does not explain them. To explain a trial would be to destroy its object, which is that of calling forth simple faith and implicit obedience. If we knew why the Lord sent us this or that trial, it would thereby cease to be a trial either of faith or of patience.
>
> —ALFRED EDERSHEIM, DD

The book of Job is concerned with the question of suffering. But more important, it is consumed with the question of suffering as it stands under the umbrella of God's sovereignty. Under the umbrella of God's sovereignty, we do not need to understand the meaning of our trials. Under the umbrella of His sovereignty, we can concern ourselves with the weightier issue of our faith — and of its strength and resiliency.

November, 1873. Horatio Spafford, a successful Chicago lawyer and businessman, watched as his wife and four daughters boarded the SS *Ville du Havre*, bound for England. Delayed by unexpected business, he planned to follow in a few days to join his family. During the family's stay in England, Spafford also planned to accompany and assist his good friend and evangelist, D. L. Moody, on one of his Great Britain campaigns. The family anticipated a much-needed European holiday.

Two years before, having invested heavily in real estate along Lake Michigan's shore, Spafford lost it all when the Chicago fire

When one is in very great pain and fear it is extremely difficult to pray coherently, and I could only raise my mind in anguish to God and ask for strength to hold on.

—SHEILA CASSIDY, British doctor who was arrested and tortured in Chile in 1975 for treating a revolutionary

of 1871 destroyed that area. This financial blow came only months after Spafford and his wife had buried their only son. A holiday of rest was just what Spafford and his family needed.

But on November 22, 1873, the ship carrying Spafford's family was struck by another English vessel and sank in a matter of minutes. Found clinging to a piece of debris, Mrs. Spafford was barely conscious. She and the other survivors were taken by rescue ship to England, and en route, she sent her husband a message: "Saved, alone."

Spafford left to join his grief-stricken wife in England. While sailing through the portion of sea where it was believed his daughters had drowned, he penned these words — words that would become one of our most profound hymns of faith and trust in God in the midst of overwhelming grief:[5]

> When peace, like a river, attendeth my way
> When sorrows like sea billows roll
> Whatever my lot, Thou hast taught me to say
> It is well, it is well with my soul.
>
> Tho Satan should buffet, tho trials should come
> Let this blest assurance control
> That Christ hath regarded my helpless estate
> And hath shed His own blood for my soul.
>
> My sin — O the bliss of this glorious tho't
> My sin, not in part, but the whole
> Is nailed to the cross, and I bear it no more
> Praise the Lord, praise the Lord, O my soul!
>
> And Lord, haste the day when my faith shall be sight
> The clouds be rolled back as a scroll:
> The trump shall resound and the Lord shall descend
> Even so it is well with my soul.[6]

The tears streamed down, and I let them flow as freely as they would, making of them a pillow for my heart. On them it rested.
—SAINT AUGUSTINE OF HIPPO, author of *Confessions*

What do you feel after reading this story?

Suffering under the umbrella of God's sovereignty is at the same time terrifying and hopeful. We want desperately to be able to say, "it is well with my soul" when "sorrows like sea billows roll." But how do we get to that point? Job might answer, "not easily, not quickly, and not by our own power." Only when God's blazing glory, power, and being invade our souls and dispel every other inferior notion about Him can we respond with that kind of faith.

With Job we must learn to say,

> I have heard of You by the hearing of the ear;
> But now my eye sees You;
> Therefore I retract,
> And I repent in dust and ashes. (42:5-6)

Knowing and trusting God more fully is a lifelong journey. How are you coming along in your travels?

This only we may be assured of, that if tomorrow brings a cross, He who sends it can and will send grace to bear it.
—J. C. RYLE, nineteenth-century minister

What prayer would be most fitting for you to pray in light of this study? One of repentance? Thanksgiving? Petition? Praise? Stop and do so now.

MEMORY VERSE

> Naked I came from my mother's womb,
> And naked I shall return there.
> The LORD gave and the LORD has taken away.
> Blessed be the name of the LORD.
>
> JOB 1:21

JOB

[Sovereignty of God]

REVIEW

1. The theme of Job is the suffering of man and the _____sovereignty_____ of God.

2. The Prominent Player in the book is _____Job_____ .

3. Chapter 42 is our Crucial Chapter because Job repented and God_____blessed_____ him.

4. Our Notable Feature is the book's description of God's sovereignty over all _____creation_____ .

5. "Naked I came from my mother's womb,

   And naked I shall return there.

   The LORD gave and the LORD has taken away.

   _____Blessed_____ be the name of the LORD."

JOB 1:<u>21</u>

PSALMS

[Life of Worship]

One thing I have asked from the LORD, that I shall seek:

That I may dwell in the house of the LORD all the days of my life,

To behold the beauty of the LORD

And to meditate in His temple.

PSALM 27:4

PSALMS
[Life of Worship]

INTRODUCTION

Worship has always been at the center of man's relationship with His Creator. As the people of Israel sought to worship God, hymns were composed to express their feelings through song. These hymns were used in the temple worship as multitudes gathered and sung alone as men of God cried out to Him. In praise and adoration, conflict and pain, repentance and remorse, and dryness of soul, the faithful addressed their God. The book of Psalms is a lyric, poetical book written to be accompanied by instruments.

The time span of these writings covers almost 1,000 years. Moses may have been the author of one of the Psalms (Psalm 90), dating back to the time of The Pentateuch. Nearly half were written by King David during the time of The Kingdom Books, and it is possible that Ezra authored one or more of them during the post-exilic period.

Today the book of Psalms still stands as one of the most beloved books ever written. Of the sixty-six biblical books, Psalms is the longest and most widely read book in the Bible. A wide range of topics and diverse emotions are expressed in these 150 lyric poems. So as we begin our study of the book of Psalms, it is our prayer that you will drink deeply from these beautiful hymns to our God, Creator, and Father.

PSALMS
[Life of Worship]

OVERVIEW

WHO: Authors: The majority of the psalms (73) are attributed to David; other attributed authors include the sons of Korah (12), Asaph (12), Solomon (2), Heman (1), Ethan (1), and Moses (1); the remaining 48 are anonymous

WHAT: The Jewish hymnal; a collection of poetry to be sung as praise and worship in the temple; literally: "Poetry to be sung to stringed accompaniment"

WHEN: Most were written during the reigns of Solomon and David

WHERE: Sung in Israel about God and the nation

WHY: Psalms is a collection of praises exclaiming God's attributes and character

I. THE FIVE PARTS OF PSALMS

A. Book 1 relates to _____man_____ (Psalms 1–41).

B. Book 2 relates to the _____nation_____ (Psalms 42–72).

C. Book 3 relates to the _____sanctuary_____ (Psalms 73–89).

D. Book 4 relates to the _____Earth_____ (Psalms 90–106).

E. Book 5 relates to the _____Word of God_____ (Psalms 107–150).

II. THE FINER POINTS OF PSALMS

A. Psalms gives us many descriptions of who God is and are known as God's character or _____attributes_____.

B. Psalms encourages us with words of _____hope_____ and _____comfort_____.

C. Psalms contains personal prayers of admission of sin called _____confession_____.

D. Psalms is a heartfelt collection of truthful feelings (both good and bad) and is, therefore, considered a book of _____honesty_____.

E. Psalms contains much _____instruction_____ on how to live a
   righteous life.

F. Psalms is full of __prophecy~~instruction~~__ describing future events, especially
   regarding the life and death of the promised Messiah.

G. Psalms is considered a book of _thanksgiving_ and calls on us to
   be grateful for all blessings.

APPLICATION

The book of Psalms is one of the most familiar and best-loved books of the
Old Testament. It is a book of encouragement and comfort that expresses
joy and victory as well as sorrow and failure. We turn to the Psalms when
we don't know where else to go.

VERSES TO READ IN THE PSALMS
WHEN YOU DON'T KNOW WHERE ELSE TO TURN

For Comfort:
   Psalm 4:3
   Psalm 18:1-3
   Psalm 23
   Psalm 24
   Psalm 32:23-24

For Hope:
   Psalm 27
   Psalm 34:18-19
   Psalm 37:3-5
   Psalm 38:15
   Psalm 40:1-3
   Psalm 119
   Psalm 121

For Confession:
   Psalm 32
   Psalm 51

For Instruction:
   Psalm 1
   Psalm 19:14
   Psalm 46:10
   Psalm 141:3-4

For Prophecy Regarding the Messiah:
   Psalm 22
   Psalm 69
   Psalm 110

For Thanksgiving:
   Psalm 9:1-2
   Psalm 103

For Help with Anxiety:
   Psalm 27:1-3
   Psalm 40:1-3
   Psalm 119
   Psalm 121

For Help with Depression:
   Psalm 27
   Psalm 30:5
   Psalm 40:1-3

For Help with Fear:
   Psalm 4:8
   Psalm 34:4-7
   Psalm 103
   Psalm 121

For Forgiveness:
   Psalm 32
   Psalm 103

PSALMS
[Life of Worship]

LEARNING FOR LIFE

1. Review The Poetical Books of Job and Psalms. Identify where these two books fit into The Historical Books. What is the main theme of each book, and what purpose do these books serve?

2. Look at Psalm 23. What are some of the truths you learn about God from this psalm? What do you learn about yourself?

3. The Psalms often give an honest view of the poet's feelings as he cries out to God. Are you able to be this honest with God? Why or why not?

4. What benefits do we receive when we praise and worship God?

PSALMS
[Life of Worship]

DAY ONE

COMPLETE READ: Chapters 1–41
QUICK READ: Chapter 34

THE BIG PICTURE

> The Holy Spirit has represented to the life all the griefs, sorrows, fears, doubts, hopes, cares, anxieties, in short, all the stormy emotions by which human minds are wont to be agitated.
>
> —JOHN CALVIN

Testimonies abound of the incredible power of the Psalms to bring comfort, strength, hope, and help for emotional and spiritual survival. It seems not one of the vast array of emotions we experience is left out.

In 1977 at the height of the Cold War, Anatoly Shcharansky, a brilliant young mathematician and chess player, was arrested by the KGB for his repeated attempts to immigrate to Israel. He spent thirteen years inside the Soviet gulag. From morning to evening Shcharansky read and studied all 150 psalms (in Hebrew). "What does this give me?" he asked in a letter. "Gradually, my feeling of great loss and sorrow changes to one of bright hopes."

Shcharansky so cherished his book of Psalms, in fact, that when guards took it away from him, he lay in the snow, refusing to move, until they returned it. During those thirteen years, his wife traveled around the world campaigning for his release. Accepting an honorary degree on his behalf, she told the university audience, "In a lonely cell in Chisopol prison, locked alone with the Psalms of David, Anatoly found expression for his

Worship, then, is not a part of the Christian life; it is the Christian life.

—GERALD VANN, twentieth-century Dominican Priest

innermost feelings in the outpourings of the King of Israel thousands of years ago."[1]

The book of Psalms is the glorious worship book, or hymnbook, of the temple. But that's not all. It is a hymnbook of great *honesty* — honesty of emotion as the psalmist experiences life and honesty of expression as the psalmist addresses God. Miss this facet, and we miss a great gift of God to us. The book of Psalms pictures a life of honest worship.

At first glance, the book of Psalms appears to have no organizational rhyme or reason, yet there is an overall structure: The book is divided into five books or sections.

Book	I	II	III	IV	V
Chapters	1–41	42–72	73–89	90–106	107–150
Author	Mainly David	Mainly David and Korah	Mainly Asaph	Mainly Anonymous	Mainly David
Verses	41:13	72:18-19	89:52	106:48	150:1-6

Doxology

Read the verses listed along the bottom of the chart and briefly describe the content and main emphasis of each.

41:13 *praise to God Amen Amen*

72:18-19 *praise to God Amen Amen forever*

89:52 *praise to the Lord forever Amen Amen*

106:48 *praise to God ever lasting*

150:1-6 *praise the Lord*

Combine your thoughts about each of these verses into one statement describing what they *all* seem to be about.

Praise God

AMAZING!
Of the approximately 300 direct references to the Old Testament contained in the New Testament, 116 of them are references to the Psalms.

The Psalms acquire, for those who know how to enter into them, a surprising depth, a marvelous and inexhaustible actuality. They are bread, miraculously provided by Christ, to feed those who have followed Him into the wilderness.

—THOMAS MERTON, priest and writer

Did your statement have something to do with praising God? These verses serve as a doxology ("to speak praise or glory"), bringing to conclusion each of the five books. In fact, these five doxologies gave Bible scholars the major clue that the Psalms were divided in this manner. In the lower left-hand corner of the chart, write the word *doxology*.

Remember, the Psalms were written over a period of about 1,000 years, with Moses being the earliest author (1400 BC) and Ezra possibly the latest (450 BC). David wrote seventy-three of the Psalms, forty-eight are anonymous, and various authors contributed the other twenty-nine.

In your reading of the Psalms, you may have already noticed the great variety of tone and emotion displayed there. In one chapter, the Psalmist confidently praises God for all His wondrous works. In another, he rails about the injustices of life and begs God to punish his enemies. In yet another, he pleads with God to fill his thirsty soul and save him. The different types of Psalms give this book variety, as the following chart illustrates.

Type	Lament	Thanks	Praise	Woe
Example	Psalm 13	Psalm 136	Psalm 145	Psalm 109
Major Emphasis	Petitions for Help	Gratitude for God's Acts	Praise for God and His Work	Petition for Punishment of Enemies

Finish today's study by reading Psalm 145 and reveling in your great God.

MEMORY VERSE

One thing I have asked from the LORD, that I shall seek:
That I may dwell in the house of the LORD all the days
    of my life,
To behold the beauty of the LORD
And to meditate in His temple.

PSALM 27:4

PSALMS
[Life of Worship]

DAY TWO

COMPLETE READ: Chapters 42–72
QUICK READ: Chapter 42

QUESTION
Which of the psalms is
the most well-known
to you?

A CRUCIAL CHAPTER

The Historical Books of the Old Testament (Genesis–Esther) are narrative in form — explaining the past history of God's people, Israel. The Prophetical Books (Isaiah–Malachi) are prophetic in nature — unveiling the future of God's people as revealed at that time. The Poetical Books (Job–Song of Solomon) are neither narrative nor prophecy, but poetry. They express the dealings of the people of God *with* God. Almost every facet of life is included in these expressions.

Poetry must be read differently than narrative and prophecy. There is a defining element of Hebrew poetry that, when understood even a little, will help us grasp what is being said. It is the concept of parallelism. English parallelism is based on a correspondence of sound (rhyme); Hebrew parallelism is based on a correspondence of thought. The Hebrew poet would state a proposition and then echo it in one of a number of ways in the line or lines that followed.

*That which we are
capable of feeling, we
are capable of saying.*
—MIGUEL DE CERVANTES,
writer, playwright,
and poet

The chart that follows shows the major forms of Hebrew parallelism.

Type	Synonymous	Contrasting	Progressive	Illustrative
Explanation	Say a line . . . shadow it	Say a line . . . contrast it	Say a line . . . expand it	Say a line . . . picture it
Example	Psalm 2:1	Psalm 37:9	Psalm 103:20	Psalm 42:1

As you study our Crucial Chapter, look for Hebrew parallelism and determine its type.

In her book *The Cloister Walk*, Kathleen Norris writes, "The psalms do not theologize. One reason for this is that the psalms are poetry, and poetry's function is not to explain but to offer images and stories that resonate with our lives."[2]

This is so true of our Crucial Chapter, Psalm 1. The images are clear and tangible and convey a depth of meaning and insight that mere explanatory words could not. Read Psalm 1 now.

What a wonderful place to begin our journey through the Psalms! Psalm 1 gives us a sense and sampling of what much of the book will portray:

- Contrast of the blessed man and the wicked man

- Emphasis on the law (Word) of God

- God's presence with and faithfulness to the blessed man

- The ultimate end of the wicked

- Concern about how life is lived

If there be ground for you to trust in your own righteousness, then all that Christ did to purchase salvation, and all that God did to prepare the way for it, is in vain.

—JONATHAN EDWARDS, Puritan theologian

Read Psalm 1:1 and describe the differences in the three statements.

Walk — c wicked
Stand — c sinners
Sit — c mockers

Verses 2 and 3 portray the person who avoids the three pitfalls stated in verse 1. Describe in your own words what helps him do this and, as a result, what his life is like. Remember, watch for parallelism!

prospers
yields fruit

God's yellow page

Read 1:4-6 and describe the fate of the wicked in contrast to that of the righteous.

Lord watches over the righteous
way wicked leads to destruction

How could you live "delighting in the law of the LORD"?

MEMORY VERSE

One thing I have asked from the LORD, that I shall seek:
That I may dwell in the house of the LORD all the days
   of my life,
To behold the beauty of the LORD
And to meditate in His temple.

PSALM 27:4

REVIEW IT!
Psalm 1 is our Crucial Chapter because it introduces the book of Psalms so effectively.

PSALMS
[Life of Worship]

AMAZING!
Of the 176 verses in
Psalm 119, 173 of
them speak of the Word
of God.

DAY THREE

COMPLETE READ: Chapters 73–89
QUICK READ: Chapter 86

A PROMINENT PLAYER

> In the Book of Psalms there is a universal quality which can come only from the combined expression of the spiritual experiences of men in many periods of history and in a variety of circumstances of life.
>
> —KYLE M. YATES JR., PASTOR AND TEACHER

David was one of these men who, in Yates's words, experienced "a variety of circumstances of life." He is a Prominent Player in the Psalms, having written almost half of them. In Acts 13:22, God says, "I have found David the son of Jesse, a man after My heart, who will do all My will." How we long for a commendation like that!

As a boy, David was a shepherd. Who better to plumb the depths of the relationship between the Great Shepherd and His sheep? Read Psalm 23 and visualize David writing it from the perspective of a sheep rather than a shepherd. By emphasizing the first person pronouns, you can better sense David writing from this perspective:

We know more about him than anyone else in our biblical records. . . . Nothing is held back or suppressed; the entire range of the human condition is laid out for us in the narration of David's life.

—EUGENE PETERSON, pastor and author

> The LORD is *my* shepherd,
> *I* shall not want.
> He makes *me* lie down. . . . (verses 1-2, emphasis added)

The word *psalm* means "sung to the accompaniment of a stringed instrument." David would have known all about this as well.

According to Scripture, he was quite an accomplished musician. Do you recall how his harp melodies soothed King Saul during his time of personal torment (see 1 Samuel 16:14-23)? David's musical ability also explains the abundance of musical terms used in the headings of many of the psalms. Fifty psalms are addressed to the choir director. Psalm 4, according to the heading, is expected to be played on stringed instruments. Psalm 5 was written for flute accompaniment. These directions made the poems accessible for temple worship.

But David was much more than a shepherd boy and a musician. He was also a worshiper, a soldier, a king, a seeker after God, and a man hunted by his enemies. In all of these experiences, David poured out his heart to God through the poetry of the Psalms.

Occasionally the heading of a psalm links it to a specific circumstance in David's life. Read 2 Samuel 15:13-29, which describes David's flight from his rebellious son Absalom. Now read Psalm 3, a prayer David wrote about that occasion. When you complete your reading, write down what the 2 Samuel story added to your understanding of Psalm 3.

Prayers for protection

We have seen that David was a man of talent, passion, and insight. But first and foremost he was a worshiper and a man after God's own heart. When commanded by God to "seek My face," David responded immediately with "Your face, O LORD, I shall seek" (Psalm 27:8).

PROLIFIC!
David wrote almost half of the psalms.

Alongside the story we are given his prayers, the inside of the story. For everything that happened in David's life became prayer, became the occasion for listening to and answering God. Nothing in David's life was left lying around on the surface; he took everything "to heart," interiorized it, welcomed it in God's name for God's work.

—EUGENE PETERSON, pastor and author

Our memory verse for this book is Psalm 27:4. Meditate on that verse and write down what it means to you.

REVIEW IT!
David is our Prominent Player because he wrote more of the psalms than any other person.

MEMORY VERSE

One thing I have asked from the LORD, that I shall seek:
That I may dwell in the house of the LORD all the days
of my life,
To behold the beauty of the LORD
And to meditate in His temple.

PSALM 27:4

PSALMS
[Life of Worship]

DAY FOUR

COMPLETE READ: Chapters 90–106
QUICK READ: Chapters 95–96

HERE'S A TREND
The word *praise* and its forms are used 166 times in the book of Psalms.

A NOTABLE FEATURE

> The Psalms are an anatomy of all the parts of the soul; for no one will find in himself a single feeling which the image is not reflected in this mirror.
>
> —JOHN CALVIN

Through the psalmists' words that give voice to their private lives and experiences, our own lives are revealed in the Psalms. We are there. Many times the words of the Psalms express the cry of our own souls. Yet too often we shrink back in self-consciousness or fear, thinking this honest language will be too strong for God. We fear needlessly!

In his book *The Bible Jesus Read*, Philip Yancey addresses this issue:

> The 150 psalms present a mosaic of spiritual therapy in process. Doubt, paranoia, giddiness, meanness, delight, hatred, joy, praise, vengefulness, betrayal — you can find it all in Psalms. Such strewing of emotions, which I once saw as hopeless disarray, I now see as a sign of health. From Psalms I have learned that I can rightfully bring to God whatever I feel about him. I need not paper over my failures and try to clean up my own rottenness; far better to bring those weaknesses to God, who alone has the power to heal. . . .
>
> The odd mixture of psalms of cursing, psalms of praise, and psalms of confession no longer jars me as it

Honesty leads to confession, and confession leads to change.
—RICHARD J. FOSTER, American author

once did. Instead, I am continually amazed by the spiritual wholeness of the Hebrew poets, who sought to include God in every area of life by bringing to God every emotion experienced in daily activity. One need not "dress up" or "put on a face" to meet God. There are not walled-off areas; God can be trusted with reality.

For the Hebrew poets, God represented a reality more solid than their own whipsaw emotions or the checkered history of their people. They wrestled with God over every facet of their lives, and in the end it was the very act of wrestling that proved their faith.[3]

Do you see the Psalms as Yancey does? Why or why not?

Read Psalm 13. Though we don't know for certain what circumstances prompted this heart cry, we can sense the depth of David's despair. Verses 1 and 2 are honest, heartfelt words. Rewrite these two verses as they might be spoken by a person too shy and fearful to address God as plainly as David did.

Psalm 44 creates a strong contrast within itself. In verses 1-9, the psalmist remembered the past and the work God had done. Life was so good! But in verse 9, the word *yet* creates a vivid contrast — and one that the psalmist was clearly unhappy about. What emotions might be behind the words in verses 9-26?

Write down any phrase that stands out to you as a strong but honest expression of the writer.

*rejected + humbled us
if we had forgotten our God or
seeked foreign Gods would our God
not have know.*

We have sailed too close to shore; having fallen in love with life, we have lost our thirst for the waters of Life.

—SIR FRANCIS DRAKE, English sea captain

Honest relating to God saturates the Psalms. This honesty is an avenue through which God may work to bring health to our souls. But there is another crucial thread that weaves its way through this honest dialogue. It is the admission of our helplessness and hopelessness apart from God. Peter reiterated a similar admission when Jesus asked him if he, too, would turn away because of the difficulty of following Jesus. Peter answered, "Lord, to whom shall we go? You have words of eternal life" (John 6:68).

Read Psalm 73:25-28 for a similar response by the psalmist Asaph. Explain why focused reliance on God is a necessary component of honest communication with Him.

Faith and trust in God

How would you describe your present level of honesty with God?

MEMORY VERSE

One thing I have asked from the LORD, that I shall seek:
That I may dwell in the house of the LORD all the days
    of my life,
To behold the beauty of the LORD
And to meditate in His temple.

PSALM 27:4

Psalms
[Life of Worship]

INTERESTING!
Jesus would have sung many of the psalms in the synagogue.

DAY FIVE

COMPLETE READ: Chapters 107–150
QUICK READ: Chapters 145–150

A TIMELESS PRINCIPLE

> It is not a thing which a man can decide, whether he will be a worshipper or not, a worshipper he must be; the only question is what will he worship? Every man worships — is a born worshipper.
>
> —FREDERICK W. ROBERTSON

Worship is a Timeless Principle woven into the very fabric of our nature. We were created to worship. And if we refuse or neglect to worship God, we will worship something else — something less.

Ah, Jesus, fountain of life, make me drink a cup of living water from You so that, having tasted You, I will thirst eternally for nothing but You.

—GERTRUDE THE GREAT, Benedictine and mystic writer

The Psalms is a book of worship, the hymnbook of the temple. When we read many of the psalms, we are reading the very words God's chosen people used to praise, worship, and adore Him. What an incredible resource to have at our fingertips when we so often lack the words to express ourselves to God.

In his book *Leap over a Wall,* Eugene Peterson writes,

> Worship is the strategy by which we interrupt our preoccupation with ourselves and attend to the presence of God. Worship is the time and place that we assign for deliberate attentiveness to God — not because he's confined to time and place but because our self-importance is so insidiously relentless that if we don't deliberately interrupt ourselves

regularly, we have no chance of attending to Him at all at other times and in other places.[4]

Take an opportunity to deliberately interrupt your preoccupation with yourself so that you may attend to the presence of God in worship.

Begin by reading Psalm 100. As you "enter His gates with thanksgiving," what one thing would you like to thank God for?

job
health
home
family

Read Psalm 103 — and even better, read it aloud! Write down in your own words what this psalm reveals about God that makes Him so worthy of our worship.

Creator of all

INSIGHT
In the original Hebrew language, Psalm 119 is divided into 22 sections of 8 verses each, with each verse in a section beginning with the same Hebrew letter.

God? The imagination reels.
—CHARLES AZNAVOUR

Finish by reading Psalm 145. As you read, pause to praise, bless, and thank God for who He is and what He has done, as described in this psalm of praise.

Come, let us worship and bow down,
Let us kneel before the LORD our Maker.
For He is our God,
And we are the people of His pasture and the sheep of His hand. (Psalm 95:6-7)

Eternal Father of my soul, let my first thought today be of Thee, let my first impulse be to worship Thee, let my first speech be Thy name, let my first action be to kneel before Thee in prayer.

—KAHLIL GIBRAN, mystic, poet, and artist

MEMORY VERSE

One thing I have asked from the LORD, that I shall seek:
That I may dwell in the house of the LORD all the days
    of my life,
To behold the beauty of the LORD
And to meditate in His temple.

PSALM 27:4

PSALMS
[Life of Worship]

REVIEW

1. The theme of Psalms is a life of _____honest_____ worship.

2. Psalm 1 is our Crucial Chapter because it _____introduces_____ the book of Psalms so effectively.

3. _____David_____ is our Prominent Player because he wrote more of the psalms than any other person.

4. A Notable Feature of the book of Psalms is that it clearly models the importance of sharing our most _____honest_____ thoughts and feelings with God.

5. "One thing I have asked from the LORD, that I shall seek:

   That I may dwell in the house of the LORD all the days of my life,

   To _____behold_____ the beauty of the LORD

   And to meditate in His temple."

PSALM 27:<u>4</u>

PROVERBS

[Life of Wisdom]

The fear of the LORD is the beginning of wisdom,

And the knowledge of the Holy One is understanding.

PROVERBS 9:10

THREE

PROVERBS
[Life of Wisdom]

INTRODUCTION

It is said that we live in the information age. Yet information or knowledge alone does not guarantee a better life, nor does it automatically provide peace and contentment. God wants His children to live lives of wisdom and blessedness. The Bible in general is a great source of wisdom, and Proverbs specifically is a poetical book whose didactic nature teaches us much-needed lessons about life.

The book of Proverbs is a practical guidebook full of wisdom that can enlighten the child, the young adult, the mature adult, and the elderly. Its short sayings are nuggets of gold as we struggle to live as God wants us to in a world that values neither wisdom nor godliness.

As we begin our study, take time to slowly read through the Proverbs. These are not promises but rather are godly principles for life. Savor each one. Meditate on them, embrace them, and then begin to practice their principles. They will impact your life greatly, and as they do, you will impact those around you with this wisdom from above.

PROVERBS
[Life of Wisdom]

Observations Not promises

OVERVIEW

WHO: Author: Solomon (the majority of the book)
WHAT: Approximately 800 instructional couplets
WHEN: Written 950–700 BC; compiled nearly 200 years later by the men of Hezekiah
WHERE: Israel/Judah
WHY: To provide instruction for skillful living

I. PROVERBS FOR YOUTH (PROVERBS 1–9)

A. The main purpose of Proverbs is found in verses 1:1-6.

  1. _____Wisdom_____ — living life skillfully

  2. To know _____instruction_____ — training usually under pressure, discipline

  3. _____understanding_____ — insight, ability to discern good from evil

  4. _____Wise behavior_____ — common sense in circumstances

  5. To give _____prudence_____ — discretion, foresight, watchfulness, shrewdness

  6. To the youth _____Knowledge_____ — factual information, truth, principles

  7. And _____discretion_____ — meditation, clear and able thinking

B. The motto of the book of Proverbs is found in verse 1:7: "The _____fear_____ of the Lord. . . ."

C. The main focus is on parent/child training (Proverbs 1:8–7:27).

  1. The main form of poetry in this first section is the instructional _____sonnet_____ .

2. Most of these thematic sonnets begin with the phrase,
"___My Son___."

3. The four main characters in the sonnets are the naive, the fool, the scoffers, and the ___wise___ man.

D. The main character in the monologues is ___Wisdom___ personified (Proverbs 8–9).

II. PROVERBS OF SOLOMON (PROVERBS 10–24)

A. There are three main types of parallelisms found in the Proverbs:

1. Contrastive parallelisms — where opposite thoughts are put together. They are signified by the word "___BUT___."

2. Completive parallelisms — the first line agrees with the second line. They usually have the word "___AND___" between the first and the second sentences.

3. Comparative parallelisms — compare godliness with ungodliness. They often have the word "___Than___" helping the sentence to agree.

B. There are two types of analogy and imagery found in the Proverbs:

1. Epigrams — short, ___witty___ statements or sayings

2. Aphorisms — short, ___wise___ statements or sayings

III. PROVERBS COMPILED BY HEZEKIAH (PROVERBS 25–31)

A. The Thirteen ___sayings___ of Agur (Proverbs 30)

1. Agur was thought to be an Ishmaelite.

2. Agur's sayings were verbally communicated and rhetorical in nature.

3. Agur reminded the listener that only God is wise.

B. The ___oracle___ of Lemuel (Proverbs 31:1-9)

1. Lemuel was believed to be an Arabian king.

2. Lemuel's mother gave him this wise advice verbally.

3. Lemuel's charge was for leaders. *poem*

C. The _____acrostic_____ of the Wise Woman (Proverbs 31:10-31)

1. An acrostic is a written poem or series of lines in which certain letters form a motto, message, or sequence.

2. This acrostic has twenty-two verses where the first letter of each verse consecutively follows the complete Hebrew alphabet.

3. This acrostic portrays the virtuous wife.

APPLICATION

We need godly wisdom to live godly lives in an ungodly world.

PROVERBS
[Life of Wisdom]

LEARNING FOR LIFE

1. Beginning with Job, build the foundation for the book of Proverbs.

2. What is the author's main objective in this book?

3. The word *wisdom* means "to live life skillfully." Why would skillful living be important to God? Why would it be important for His people?

4. Who is called "wisdom from God" in the New Testament? (See 1 Corinthians 1:30.)

5. How do you feel about the portrayal of women in the book of Proverbs?

6. What has challenged you the most in this book? Why?

PROVERBS
[Life of Wisdom]

DAY ONE

COMPLETE READ: Chapters 1–9
QUICK READ: Chapter 4

FACT
The New Testament
alludes to or quotes
Proverbs at least
fourteen times.

THE BIG PICTURE

> A proverb is a short, pregnant sentence or phrase whose meaning is applicable in many situations, with imagery or striking verbal form to assist the memory. It has been well described as having shortness, sense, and salt.
> — R. B. Y. SCOTT, *THE WAY OF WISDOM*

We are familiar with our culture's proverbs — one-line statements of how things are or will be if a certain course is taken.

If the shoe fits, wear it.

A rolling stone gathers no moss.

The Bible has its own set of proverbs, but they tend to be two-line statements:

> There is a way which seems right to a man,
> But its end is the way of death. (Proverbs 16:25)

He is not wise to me who is wise in words only, but he who is wise in deeds.

—SAINT GREGORY I, pope of the sixth century

Because of the two-line structure, we know the proverbs in the Bible use Hebrew poetic parallelism, which we discussed on Day Two in our study of the Psalms. In fact, the word *proverb* means comparison, simile, or parallel. A proverb uses a comparison to make a pithy but potent statement about the practical realities of daily life.

INTERESTING!
Teaching through
proverbs is likely the
most ancient form of
instruction.

Some proverbs require a time of reflection to gain the benefits of their meaning:

> He who pursues righteousness and loyalty
> Finds life, righteousness and honor. (Proverbs 21:21)

Other proverbs are so straightforward and provocative that we feel their impact immediately:

> Better is a dry morsel and quietness with it
> Than a house full of feasting with strife. (Proverbs 17:1)

Still others are so rich with image that they bring a chuckle:

> As a ring of gold in a swine's snout
> So is a beautiful woman who lacks discretion. (Proverbs 11:22)

Regardless of its style, every proverb conveys a time-tested truth. There are no fads or shallow platitudes here. And if we follow the advice of these proverbs, they will bring health to our souls.

Proverbs 1:1 states that this book is "the proverbs of Solomon the son of David, king of Israel." Although Solomon did not write all of the material in the book, he wrote such a major part of it that it was reasonable to name him as the author. The material was finally compiled and editorialized by King Hezekiah of Judah some 250 years later. In general terms, the book can be divided as follows:

There is often wisdom under a shabby cloak.

—Latin proverb

Chapters 1–9	Chapters 10–29	Chapters 30–31
Introduction to Proverbs	Collection of Proverbs	Appendixes to Proverbs
Praise of Wisdom	Particulars of Wisdom	Patterns of Wisdom

The purpose of the book, which we will investigate on Day Two, is clearly described in 1:2-7, and it revolves around the concept of wisdom. As the chart indicates, wisdom is praised (and personified) in chapters 1–9, detailed in chapters 10–29, and vividly demonstrated for us in the last two chapters.

The Hebrew term for wisdom encompasses more than mere intelligence and shrewdness. It means skill in living life. It means knowing how to apply intelligence in the practical realities of daily life and to exercise shrewdness in the challenges of typical human existence.

Read Exodus 28:2-3 and 36:1-2, remembering that the words *skill* and *skillful* are words that mean wisdom. What do these words in these contexts tell you about the nature of wisdom?

Just as skilled or wise craftsmen have the ability to perform their craft well, skilled or wise people have the ability to live their lives well. A life of skillful living is the theme of the book of Proverbs. As you read and study Proverbs this week, look for those areas of life where God has given you "skill" and rejoice in them. In areas in which you sense you are less "skilled," ask God to teach and change you.

MEMORY VERSE

The fear of the LORD is the beginning of wisdom,
And the knowledge of the Holy One is understanding.

SPAN PROVERBS 9:10

Wise men change their minds, fools never.

—English proverb

REVIEW IT!
The theme of Proverbs
is a life of skillful
living.

PROVERBS
[Life of Wisdom]

DAY TWO

COMPLETE READ: Chapters 10–15
QUICK READ: Chapter 1

A CRUCIAL CHAPTER

Only a fool tests the depth of the water with both feet.
—African proverb

From David's closet (in Psalms), consecrated to prayer, we now pass into Solomon's school of wisdom (in Proverbs), to admire the greatest of philosophers in the son of the greatest of theologians.

—C. B. MICHAELIS

When we move from Psalms to Proverbs, we don't leave Psalms behind, or even Job for that matter. The book of Proverbs is a transition book in the poetical section of the Old Testament, looking back to the previous two books and looking ahead to Ecclesiastes and Song of Solomon. The chart that follows shows this.

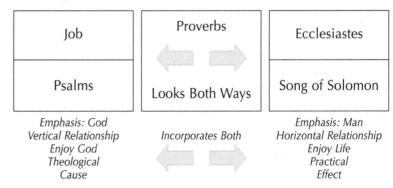

Job	Proverbs	Ecclesiastes
Psalms	Looks Both Ways	Song of Solomon

Emphasis: God		*Emphasis: Man*
Vertical Relationship	*Incorporates Both*	*Horizontal Relationship*
Enjoy God		*Enjoy Life*
Theological		*Practical*
Cause		*Effect*

Chapter 1, particularly verses 2-7, strongly demonstrates this as well. These six verses also:

- Describe the purpose of Proverbs

- Introduce three of the four major characters of the book
- Provide a motto for the book

This makes chapter 1 our Crucial Chapter.

The purpose of Proverbs is to teach and convince the reader of the importance of wisdom. The first few verses of chapter 1 indicate that this kind of wisdom — living skillfully — includes a number of components, such as the following:

- "To know wisdom and instruction" (verse 2):
  - Discipline or training
  - Indicates the seriousness of wisdom
- "To discern the sayings of understanding" (verse 2):
  - Insight — the ability to discern the true nature and significance of things
  - Indicates the depth of wisdom
- "To receive instruction in wise behavior" (verse 3):
  - Common sense — what to do in a particular circumstance
  - Indicates the value of wisdom
- "To give prudence" (verse 4):
  - Discretion, foresight, watchfulness
  - Indicates the alertness of wisdom
- "To the youth knowledge" (verse 4):
  - Factual information, true ideas and principles
  - Indicates the objectivity of wisdom
- "And discretion" (verse 4):
  - Meditation, clear thinking
  - Indicates the responsibility of wisdom

These very practical components of wisdom also carry a high priority in the books of Ecclesiastes and Song of Solomon.

COUNT 'EM
The words *fool*, *foolishness*, and *folly* are mentioned almost 160 times in Proverbs.

Wisdom comes only by suffering.
—Greek proverb

In this expansion of the concept of wisdom, what impressed you as insightful? Helpful? New?

Solomon's teaching will address four different kinds of individuals, all of whom were introduced in chapter 1, three of them in the first seven verses.

NAIVE	FOOL	SCOFFER	WISE MAN
Gullible and Wayward	*Despises Wisdom and Instruction*	*Mocks and Knows It All*	*Accepts and Increases in Wisdom*
1:4,22,32	1:7,22,32	1:22	1:5

When you stray from the path of the wise man, which of the other three characters do you most likely resemble? Explain your answer.

Verse 7 is generally considered to be the motto or overall guide for the book. Our memory verse is Proverbs 9:10 and is very similar. It is in this concept of "the fear of the LORD" that Proverbs most clearly points back to Job and Psalms. This truth occurs specifically in these books over sixty times. Read, for example, Psalm 111:10.

What does "the fear of the LORD" mean to you?

Do you feel any tension in your understanding of it? If so, explain it.

MEMORY VERSE

The fear of the LORD is the beginning of wisdom,
And the knowledge of the Holy One is understanding.

PROVERBS 9:10

REVIEW IT!
Chapter 1 is a Crucial Chapter because it spells out the purpose of the book, introduces us to the four main characters of the book, and gives us the book's motto.

PROVERBS
[Life of Wisdom]

DAY THREE

COMPLETE READ: Chapters 16–21
QUICK READ: Chapter 17

A PROMINENT PLAYER

In *Stories for the Heart*, Leslie Flynn tells the following story:

> The children worked long and hard on their own little cardboard shack. It was to be a special spot — a clubhouse — where they could meet in solemn assembly or just laugh, play games, and fool around. As they thought long and hard about their rules, they came up with three rather perceptive ones:
> 1. Nobody act big.
> 2. Nobody act small.
> 3. Everybody act medium.[1]

To these children, to act medium most likely meant to act *just right*. In adult terms, acting medium would mean to not think too highly or too badly of yourself. Just *medium*.

At a crucial time in his life, Solomon, the author of most of the book of Proverbs, acted just right. In acting just right, he asked for and received the gift of wisdom displayed in Proverbs.

Read 1 Kings 3:3-14 and write down your responses to the following questions.

How could Solomon have "acted big" in this encounter?

How could he have "acted small" in this encounter?

A GOOD CHANCE
Solomon probably
wrote the book of
Proverbs during his
middle-age years.

Read 1 Kings 4:29-34 and describe in your own words the breadth of wisdom that Solomon received from God.

In 1 Kings 10:1-10 we see that Solomon's wisdom commanded respect in someone who had only heard of him from afar. How is Solomon's wisdom described in this passage?

Nowhere are there more hiding places than in the heart.
—German proverb

Because God granted wisdom to King Solomon, we have the books of Proverbs, Ecclesiastes, and Song of Solomon — treasuries of skillful living distilled for our benefit.

There is a certain tragedy in this story, however. First Kings 11:4 states, "For when Solomon was old, his wives turned his heart away after other gods; and his heart was not wholly devoted to the LORD his God, as the heart of David his father had been."

Ironically, in Proverbs Solomon speaks often about the heart. He knew how critical the heart was to walking wisely with God and living skillfully. He warned in Proverbs 27:19,

> As in water face reflects face,
> So the heart of man reflects man.

And he wrote in Proverbs 3:5-6,

> Trust in the LORD with all your heart
>> And do not lean on your own understanding.
>> In all your ways acknowledge Him,
>> And He will make your paths straight.

And yet Solomon strayed. His heart was captured by other things, even though he knew better.

Read Proverbs 17:3 and 21:2 and state the truth Solomon knew about how God deals with people's hearts.

Solomon neglected his own advice. How sad that this advice could have kept him from losing part of his heart to other gods. Read Proverbs 4:20-23. What might it mean to "watch over your heart with all diligence"?

Do you see any danger spots in your own heart? If so, what are they? Will you agree with God about them and ask Him to help you "watch over your heart with all diligence"?

It would be a device of conceit to insist that purity of the heart is the exclusive test of piety [godliness]. Perfect purity is something we rarely know how to obtain or how to retain. No one can claim to have purged all the dross even from his finest desire. The self is finite, but selfishness is infinite. God asks for the heart.

—ABRAHAM JOSHUA HESCHEL, twentieth-century Jewish theologian

REVIEW IT!
Solomon, our Prominent Player and the author of Proverbs, failed at times to apply his own wisdom.

MEMORY VERSE

The fear of the LORD is the beginning of wisdom,
And the knowledge of the Holy One is understanding.
PROVERBS 9:10

PROVERBS
[Life of Wisdom]

INTERESTING!
Most of Solomon's
marriages were
probably political
arrangements.

DAY FOUR

COMPLETE READ: Chapters 22–26
QUICK READ: Chapter 31

A NOTABLE FEATURE

The book of Proverbs talks a lot about wives and mothers, but it also speaks to women in general. Whatever your specific role, don't miss the character traits to be developed in these passages.

A Notable Feature of the book of Proverbs is chapter 31, verses 10-31. This passage extolls the virtues of the excellent woman. It calls women to virtue, industry, faithfulness, and ministry and demonstrates the high respect with which all virtuous women should be honored.

Be honest. When you read Proverbs 31, are you encouraged or intimidated? Why?

The more I considered Christianity, the more I found that while it had established a rule and order, the chief aim of that order was to give room for good things to run wild.

—G. K. CHESTERTON, British author

In her book *The Allure of Hope*, Jan Meyers writes, "The picture painted in Proverbs 31 used to make me tired. I could never be that woman, so why bother?" But she continues,

> Then I realized that this beautiful proverb is written about a woman who is confident in something other than herself. She is well cared for. She doesn't use the care she's receiving to foster slothfulness. She is a warrior — strong, dignified, undergirded with mission. But she remembers the call to be an artist, and she goes about it on this side of the garden [Eden] with courage as she remembers who is taking care of

her. Her nobility of spirit flows from a conviction that she cannot take care of herself.[2]

Here we find a woman who believes with all her heart that she is loved by a God who knows and cares for her. And she depends on her God, not on herself. Now that is encouraging! Keep this profound insight in mind as you study today.

Before looking at chapter 31, it's important to see its contrast. The following verses picture a woman who depends on *herself*. Describe how she would be different if instead she depended on her *God*.

11:22

12:4

14:1

21:19

25:24

27:15

These verses about the foolish and contentious woman are useful for warning and contrast. But much more space is given in Proverbs to the excellent woman, as described in the following verses.

> An excellent wife is the crown of her husband. (12:4)

> The wise woman builds her house. (14:1)

> A prudent wife is from the LORD. (19:14)

These verses whet our appetite for more on the subject of virtue and point to chapter 31, verses 10-31, where we see a fuller description of this admirable and honorable woman.

GRAMMAR LESSON
In Hebrew, the word *wisdom* is a feminine noun.

You may not know this, but Christianity isn't meant to make you into an efficient, moral woman. Are we meant to change as Christ stuns us with His forgiveness? Absolutely. But the transformation that comes, impacting who we are as women, does so naturally as an afterthought of God's love for us, surprising us as it shows up.
—JAN MEYERS, speaker and author

As you read these verses, what strikes you most about this woman?

Her husband is mentioned three times in verses 11, 23, and 28-29. What is said about him, and how does this reflect upon her?

What does the second half of verse 10 mean to you?

As you look back over these verses, describe this woman in your own words. How are you similar to her? How are you different?

Finally, remember this important point: You are reading about a mature woman who has journeyed far with God. All of us are works in progress — in different stages of life and growing at different rates. Be realistic in your expectations, but don't dismiss lightly the standard that this passage provides. What from this study has challenged and motivated you? Tell God what you are thinking and feeling right now.

REVIEW IT!
Our Notable Feature is the description of the excellent woman who fears God in Proverbs 31.

MEMORY VERSE

The fear of the LORD is the beginning of wisdom,
And the knowledge of the Holy One is understanding.

PROVERBS 9:10

PROVERBS
[Life of Wisdom]

DAY FIVE

COMPLETE READ: Chapters 27–31
QUICK READ: Chapters 8–9

A TIMELESS PRINCIPLE

Someone once asked Corrie ten Boom how she could possibly handle all the compliments and praise that were constantly heaped upon her, without becoming proud. She said she looked at each compliment as a beautiful long-stemmed flower given to her. She smelled it for a moment and then put it into a vase with the others. Each night, just before retiring, she took the beautiful bouquet and handed it over to God saying, "Thank you, Lord, for letting me smell the flowers; they all belong to you." She had discovered the secret to genuine humility.[3]

This is wisdom in action, skill in living.

Matthew Henry is a well-known Bible commentator. One day he was robbed and that evening made the following entry in his diary: Let me be thankful — First, because I was never robbed before. Second, because although they took my wallet they did not take my life. Third, because although they took my all, it was not much. And fourth, because it was I who was robbed, not I who robbed.[4]

Again, this is wisdom in action, skill in living.

Remember our definition of wisdom, or skill in living, from Day Two? It is as follows:

INTERESTING! Wisdom is personalized in chapter 8 and seems almost divine. Compare this passage to 1 Corinthians 1:30.

To be a witness does not consist in engaging in propaganda, nor even in stirring people up, but in being a living mystery. It means to live in such a way that one's life would not make sense if God did not exist.

—EMMANUEL CARDINAL SUHARD, twentieth-century archbishop of Paris

A proverb states what is generally, though not invariably, true. Life is full of exceptions to generalities, but exceptions don't constitute proverbial statements.

- Instruction — requiring discipline and training
- Understanding — showing insight and discernment
- Wise behavior — practicing common sense in every circumstance
- Prudence — displaying foresight and watchfulness
- Knowledge — gaining factual information and true ideas
- Discretion — applying meditation and clear thinking

Notice how much of this definition is implicit in the illustrations from the lives of Corrie ten Boom and Matthew Henry. Wisdom is very practical. It carries day-to-day, moment-to-moment relevance.

For the person who pursues wisdom, delights are abundant. Spend some time reading and meditating on Proverbs 3:1-26. These verses describe many delightful benefits of wisdom. Find as many of them as you can and write them down in your own words.

One cannot simply open his eyes and see. The work of understanding involves not only dialectic, but a long labor of acceptance, obedience, liberty and love.

—THOMAS MERTON, Catholic priest

Which one or two of the benefits you just recorded delight you most? Explain why.

So is our new assignment in life to evaluate everything we say and do? To make wise choices every day? To pursue skillful living with gusto? While pursuing skillful living *is* a noble venture, anyone can do that even if she doesn't believe in God. But to succeed — to really *gain* true wisdom — requires something far beyond our own ability. And that's what our Timeless Principle is all about. Corrie ten Boom, Matthew Henry, and others who *truly* lived skillfully knew a secret: *The fear of the Lord is the beginning of wisdom.*

Look again at Proverbs 1:7 (our motto for the book) and 9:10 (our memory verse). Do you see the emphasis? We can wear ourselves out chasing hard after wisdom, but unless we begin with "the fear of the LORD," we chase in vain. Unless we begin with "the fear of the LORD," we strive for skillful living based on our finite attempts, rather than God's endless supply of power in our lives.

Until we are humbled at His awesomeness, made speechless at His holiness, and become awestruck at His majesty; until we quake at His wrath against sin and tremble at His incredible power; until we are overcome by His unending mercy and captured by His unsearchable love — in short, until we arrive at that place where we grasp that He is God and we are not, or at least are on the way — we pursue wisdom in vain. Because the beginning of wisdom is "the fear of the LORD."

Take time to talk to God about your journey toward learning to fear Him. How are you doing at becoming a person of wisdom, skilled in living life?

MEMORY VERSE

The fear of the LORD is the beginning of wisdom,
And the knowledge of the Holy One is understanding.

PROVERBS 9:10

My child, apart from Me, you have no wisdom, and life serves no purpose. My Spirit, the breath of the Almighty, blows through your heart, soul, and mind, and fills it with heaven's thoughts and desires. Every time a positive thought is born; each time your heart swells in love toward another; whenever you experience an "aha!" moment of truth; the breath of the Almighty has been at work.

—REBECCA BARLOW JORDAN, author of *Daily in Your Presence*

PROVERBS
[Life of Wisdom]

REVIEW

1. The theme of Proverbs is a life of _____ living.

2. Chapter 1 is a Crucial Chapter because it spells out the _____ of the book, introduces us to the four main characters of the book, and gives us the book's motto.

3. _____ , our Prominent Player and the author of Proverbs, failed at times to apply his own wisdom.

4. Our Notable Feature is the description of the _____ woman who fears God in Proverbs 31.

5. "The fear of the LORD is the beginning of _____ , And the knowledge of the Holy One is understanding."

PROVERBS 9:_____

ECCLESIASTES

[Life of Enjoyment]

The conclusion, when all has been heard, is:

fear God and keep His commandments,

because this applies to every person.

ECCLESIASTES 12:13

FOUR

ECCLESIASTES
[Life of Enjoyment]

INTRODUCTION

The book of Job deals with the problem of suffering, Psalms gives us hymns of worship, and Proverbs pours out heavenly wisdom. The little book of Ecclesiastes is a philosophical book that asks, "What is life all about?" "What really counts in this life?" and "What truly satisfies the heart of man?" It is a didactic poem that teaches lessons about life.

The author had ample opportunity to explore the many pleasures of this world, and each exploration promised happiness and contentment. Yet he found them all lacking. After a life of pursuit — a life of vanity — he concluded that life apart from God is empty, and that this world offers nothing that ultimately satisfies.

Solomon's conclusion was, "Vanity of vanities! All is vanity," unless man looks at life through a heavenly perspective. Only then will he find meaning, wholeness, contentment, joy, and satisfaction. As we study this book, you may find that you have already concluded what the "Preacher" is talking about. If so, you might want to give thanks to our God who truly satisfies.

ECCLESIASTES
[Life of Enjoyment]

youversion

OVERVIEW

WHO: Author: Solomon
Main Character: "The Preacher" (Solomon)

WHAT: The meaning of life and how to find enjoyment

WHEN: About 935 BC

WHERE: On earth, or "under the sun"

WHY: To demonstrate that life "under the sun" is vanity, or meaningless, without God

I. THE PROBLEM: LIFE WITHOUT GOD IS MEANINGLESS (ECCLESIASTES 1–6)

A. Solomon sought meaning in:

1. Wisdom — He excelled in science and knowledge.

2. Wine — He tried all pleasure and laughter.

3. Works — He achieved great accomplishments and business success.

4. Wealth — He accumulated possessions including gold and servants.

5. Women — He enjoyed the pleasure of men.

Conclusion: He hated life because everything is futile (Ecclesiastes 2:17).

B. Solomon saw emptiness in:

1. Reality — We're in time ending in death, but eternity is in our heart.

2. Relationships — We oppress others, compete, and are unfaithful.

3. Religion — We make empty prayers and vows.

4. Riches — We die and leave our riches or lose them.

II. THE SOLUTION: LIFE WITH GOD IS MEANINGFUL (ECCLESIASTES 7–12)

A. God gives life meaning.

1. God is in _control_ — man is not!

2. God knows the _future_ — man does not!

3. God gives _enjoyment_ — things and pleasures do not.

   a. We are to enjoy our _work_ — for it is God's gift.

   b. We are to enjoy our _wealth_ — it too is God's gift.

   c. We are to enjoy our _wife_ (husband) — for this is our reward.

B. God gives death meaning.

1. Death is going to our eternal _home_ (Ecclesiastes 12:5).

2. At death our body returns to the earth but our spirit returns to _God_ (Ecclesiastes 12:7).

APPLICATION

The conclusion is: Fear God and keep His commandments.

Wholeness !

ECCLESIASTES
[Life of Enjoyment]

LEARNING FOR LIFE

1. Give a brief overview of the poetical books we have covered thus far.

2. What are some of the pursuits of happiness women engage in today?

3. Read Ecclesiastes 3:11. Can you give a personal example of God making beautiful something that was difficult, hurtful, or sorrowful?

4. "Vanity of vanities! All is vanity." Have you seen this in your own life? In what ways?

5. Solomon sought a full, abundant life. Who does the Bible say is the giver of such a life? (See John 10:10; Ephesians 3:19.)

ECCLESIASTES
[Life of Enjoyment]

JUST A THOUGHT
Ecclesiastes is the most philosophical book of the Bible.

DAY ONE

COMPLETE READ: Chapters 1–2
QUICK READ: Chapter 1:1-2

THE BIG PICTURE

Ecclesiastes is the sphinx of Hebrew literature.

—UNKNOWN

The book was a renegade from the traditional faith of Israel.

—WESLEY J. FEARST

Ecclesiastes is the most mysterious book in the Bible.

—GRAHAM SCROGGIE

Ecclesiastes is perhaps the most perplexing and confusing book of the Bible to the average reader.

—MERRILL F. UNGER

One life, a little gleam of time between two eternities.

—THOMAS CARLYLE, Scottish writer

Do these words encourage you to jump in and study our book for this week? Perhaps not, but don't be discouraged! Ecclesiastes *is* a strange book, and its study will require some effort on our part, but what we will gain will be invaluable. This week we will untangle its message and see that its truth is as relevant and revolutionary today as at any time in history.

Although there is considerable debate over the authorship of this book, the best candidate appears to be Solomon. Chapter 1:1, which says, "the son of David, king in Jerusalem," is strong evidence for his authorship. The name *Ecclesiastes* derives from a

Greek word meaning "assembly," thus we get the translation "Preacher" in verse 1:1 — "the words of the Preacher." So, the book is a series of sermons preached by Solomon, most likely toward the end of his life between 935 and 931 BC.

The material in the book isn't easily divided into logical sections. The Preacher's quest for meaning and purpose in life and his subsequent discoveries and philosophizing appear random. Order can be found, however, as the following chart shows.

Problem Stated	Problem Illustrated	Solutions Proposed	Solution Stated
1:1 1:11	1:12 6:12	7:1 12:8	12:9 12:14

The Preacher's dilemma was that life didn't seem to be fair or meaningful. Nothing seemed to satisfy or remain. The Preacher investigated wisdom and wealth and work and pleasure and morality and science, but nothing — absolutely nothing — produced anything worth giving his life to. Everything seemed meaningless and empty.

He summed it up at both the beginning and the end of the book: "Vanity of vanities! All is vanity" (1:2; 12:8). Pessimism saturates every page in between.

Life is an onion which one peels crying.
—French proverb

As we try to see beyond the pessimism to unravel the profound message of Ecclesiastes over the next four days, we'll study four portraits painted by the Preacher:

- A Portrait of Life (Crucial Chapter)

- A Portrait of How to Live Life (Notable Feature)

- A Portrait of God (Prominent Player)

- A Portrait of How to Live Life Before God (Timeless Principle)

Read the Quick Read, Ecclesiastes 1:1-2, again. Is there anything in your past or present that you thought would bring great meaning but has not? If so, what?

yes

MEMORY VERSE

The conclusion, when all has been heard, is: fear God and keep His commandments, because this applies to every person.

ECCLESIASTES 12:13

REVIEW IT!
The theme of Ecclesiastes is a life of genuine enjoyment.

ECCLESIASTES
[Life of Enjoyment]

DAY TWO

COMPLETE READ: Chapters 3–5
QUICK READ: Chapter 1

FACT
The word *labor* occurs
thirty-four times in the
book of Ecclesiastes.

A CRUCIAL CHAPTER

A PORTRAIT OF LIFE

The best we can hope for is unyielding despair.
—BERTRAND RUSSELL

The central neurosis of our time is emptiness.
—KARL JUNG

Nature has let us down, God seems to have left the receiver off the hook, and time is running out.
—ARTHUR KOESTLER

I live in a vacuum that is as lonely as a radio tube when the batteries are dead and there is no current to plug into.

—ERNEST HEMINGWAY

In three words I can sum up everything I've learned about life: it goes on.
—ROBERT FROST,
American poet

Clearly the theme of vanity is prevalent in modern writing. But your Quick Read for today paints the same picture. After reading chapter 1, does life seem depressing? Despairing? Hopeless? Wearisome? The word the Preacher used to describe life is *vanity*. It carries many connotations, none of them encouraging: emptiness, futility, that which is unsubstantial, fleeting, transient, a vapor, breath. Vanity is like reaching for a soap bubble: Try to grasp it and you end up with nothing — it is too fragile and fleeting to be caught.

Even the impact of the word *vanity* is doubled. "Vanity of vanities," the Hebrew superlative, states the concept in the strongest possible terms: "How utterly meaningless, how utterly meaningless! All is utterly meaningless!" This is the portrait of life the Preacher painted throughout the book. But remember, don't be discouraged — there is hope to come! For now, simply try to absorb the thoughts and feelings the Preacher was communicating.

The Preacher wove together three threads in his portrait of life: vanity (futility), "under the sun," and "striving after wind."

The word *vanity* occurs thirty-seven times in the book and six times in chapter 1. Read the following verses about vanity and summarize your thoughts about the Preacher's emphases: 2:11,15,18-19,20-23; 4:7-8; 6:12; 7:15.

> All work was in vain, meaningless
> All wisdom is in vain nothing to s
> heavily all his hard work to others
> + they will be in control

The phrase *under the sun* occurs thirty-two times in the book. Read the following verses: 1:3,9; 2:3,17,20; 3:16; 5:13; 8:9; 9:3. Before reading the next paragraph, write down what you think this phrase means and what its significance might be.

> "Everything every where
> on earth

The life without festival is a long road without an inn.

—DEMOCRITUS OF ABDERA, ancient Greek mathematician

The phrase *under the sun* is possibly the most important key to understanding the book of Ecclesiastes. It explains why everything is vanity and hopelessness. This phrase tells us that the Preacher's search for meaning was confined to this earth and its futility. He examined the material world in an attempt to solve life's riddles but never got "above the sun" to God — the only One who can provide true insight into life's mystery. What we are reading is mostly a compilation of human understanding unaided by divine understanding. Unlike King Solomon, Saint

Augustine understood the truth that "Thou hast created us, for Thyself, and our heart is restless till it finds rest in Thee."[1]

We will get to an "above the sun" perspective on Day Five. Meanwhile, the third thread the Preacher wove into his portrait of life was "striving after wind," used nine times in the book. Look at verses 1:14,17; 2:11,17; 4:16. Describe the images and/or feelings that this picturesque phrase evokes.

Man's life is like a candle in the wind, or like the frost upon the tiles.

—Chinese proverb

So that is the Preacher's portrait of life: a futile striving after the wind under the sun. In what ways can you identify with his perspective?

purpose of life
work
raise children
do good — for what purpose

Compare "vanity," "under the sun," and "striving after wind." What are their similarities and differences?

What's the point
all in vain

all encompassing

chasing
dream
purpose

MEMORY VERSE

The conclusion, when all has been heard, is: fear God and keep His commandments, because this applies to every person.

ECCLESIASTES 12:13

REVIEW IT!
Chapter 1, our Crucial Chapter, introduces the concept of "vanity of vanities."

ECCLESIASTES
[Life of Enjoyment]

DID YOU KNOW?
Ecclesiastes tells us "to eat and to drink and to be merry." But it does not say, "for tomorrow you will die!"

DAY THREE

COMPLETE READ: Chapters 6–7
QUICK READ: Chapter 6

A NOTABLE FEATURE

A PORTRAIT OF HOW TO LIVE LIFE

The Puritans are commonly portrayed as prudish, forever sad avoiders of pleasure. Kenneth Hare writes,

> The Puritan through life's sweet garden goes
> To pluck the thorn, and cast away the rose;
> And hope to please, by this peculiar whim,
> The God who fashioned it and gave it him.[2]

Joy is the most infallible sign of the presence of God.

—LEON BLOY, nineteenth-century French writer

American journalist H. L. Mencken called Puritanism "the haunting fear that someone, somewhere, may be happy."[3] Similarly, many Christ-followers feel that too much pleasure or too much fun just doesn't fit with following God. Our Notable Feature of the book of Ecclesiastes will dispel that notion, once and for all. And by the way, dreary caricatures of the Puritans are incorrect. They were serious, God-fearing folks, yet full of joy and passion.

As you perused the book of Ecclesiastes for the phrases *vanity*, *under the sun*, and *striving after wind*, you undoubtedly encountered other phrases that appeared out of place with the Preacher's primarily dismal point of view. Interestingly, those phrases, tucked amidst the doom and gloom, actually complete Solomon's portrait of how to live life.

In this second, contrasting portrait we are going to be encouraged "to eat and to drink and to be merry" — to live it up, to enjoy life. To be sure, this is still not the complete picture. On Day Five we will add the critical component without which we would be left as empty and hopeless as Solomon — even if we did eat, drink, and make merry. But before Day Five, we must first grasp the important Notable Feature of this book.

For each of the following references, summarize what the Preacher was instructing his listener to do and then state the reason given for that instruction.

2:24-25 *eat drink find satisfaction in your work - It is from the hand of God*

3:12-13 *Be happy and do good Gift from God*

3:22 *Enjoy their work Because that is their lot*

5:18-19 *eat drink find satisfaction in their toil This their lot*

8:15 *Enjoy life, nothing better to eat drink & be glad*

9:7-9 *Then joy will accompany them eat food with gladness drink your wine with joyful heart this is your lot*

11:8-9 *enjoy good years, remember the days of darkness God will bring you to judgement*

Holy joy will oil the wheels of your life's machinery. Holy joy will strengthen you for your daily labor. Holy joy will beautify you and give you an influence over the lives of others.

—CHARLES SPURGEON, British preacher

These passages are anything but morbid. Don't they sound like the kind of life we would love to live? And the best thing is that God thinks it's good. It's His desire, His gift to us. Again, this is not the whole picture, but don't miss the significance of this portrait.

How would you describe the level of pleasure and fun in your life?

So far we have viewed two portraits from the Preacher:

- His take on life: vain, empty, and meaningless
- His take on how to live life: eat, drink, and be merry

In the next lesson we turn to his portrait of God.

MEMORY VERSE

The conclusion, when all has been heard, is: fear God and keep His commandments, because this applies to every person.

ECCLESIASTES 12:13

ECCLESIASTES
[Life of Enjoyment]

DAY FOUR

COMPLETE READ: Chapters 8–9
QUICK READ: Chapter 8

A PROMINENT PLAYER

A PORTRAIT OF GOD

So far, our study of Ecclesiastes has explored the futility of life and the seemingly incongruous command to enjoy it to the hilt. But just where and how do those disparate pieces come together? There is only one answer. And through the Preacher in this book, God tells us exactly what it is: how we relate to Him. Not how we accept or bend to futility. Not how we attempt to grab opportunities to enjoy life. But how we properly understand and relate to God, because He is the Prominent Player.

In this lesson we will look at the Preacher's portrait of God and in the next lesson at his portrait of how to relate to God as we live life.

The Preacher's portrait of God is capsulized in Ecclesiastes 3:13-17. He described Him as good, in control, and just. Read the verses and summarize your thoughts about these three descriptions of God:

God Is Good (3:13; also 5:18-19; 9:7,9)

God's Gift to enjoy life

THINK ABOUT IT
Life under the sun does not work, but life under the Son does.

God is He without whom one cannot live.
—COUNT LEO TOLSTOY, Russian novelist and philosopher

NOTE
Ecclesiastes is quoted
or alluded to seven
times in the New
Testament.

God Is in Control (3:14-15; also 3:11; 7:14)

Everything Gods does will endure

God Is Just (3:16-17; also 8:11-13; 11:9)

God will bring judgement upon wickedness

*Until a man has found
God, and been found
by God, he begins at
no beginning and
works to no end.*

—H. G. WELLS, *English
novelist, journalist,
sociologist, and historian*

God is good, which encourages us to look for His blessings in the midst of life's futilities. God is in control, which encourages us to look for His sovereignty over the events taking place "under the sun." And finally, God is just, which encourages us to look for His mercy when, compared to the wicked, our efforts seem like striving after wind.

Which of these three traits of God do you need to claim the most at this stage of your life? Why?

So now we have three portraits from the Preacher:

- His take on life: vain, empty, and meaningless
- His take on how to live life: eat, drink, and be merry
- His take on God: good, in control, and just

One portrait remains: how to live life before God.

MEMORY VERSE

The conclusion, when all has been heard, is: fear God and keep His commandments, because this applies to every person.

ECCLESIASTES 12:13

REVIEW IT!
God is our Prominent Player, and He is good, in control, and just.

ECCLESIASTES
[Life of Enjoyment]

IMPORTANT
The concept of the fear
of God is mentioned
close to two hundred
times in the Bible.

DAY FIVE

COMPLETE READ: Chapters 10–12
QUICK READ: Chapter 12

A TIMELESS PRINCIPLE

A PORTRAIT OF HOW TO LIVE LIFE BEFORE GOD
The remarkable thing about fearing God, is that when
you fear God you fear nothing else, whereas if you do
not fear God, you fear everything else.
—OSWALD SANDERS

This is it! This is what the entire book of Ecclesiastes comes
down to. We need one last portrait from the Preacher, and then
our gallery for "A Life of Genuine Enjoyment" will be complete.

Fearing God is that final portrait:

*Grant, O Lord, that I
may live in Your fear,
die in Your favor, rest in
Your peace, rise in Your
power, reign in Your
glory.*
—ARCHBISHOP WILLIAM
LAUD, beheaded in 1645

The conclusion, when all has been heard, is: fear God and
keep His commandments, because this applies to every
person. (Ecclesiastes 12:13)

The Preacher has salted this truth throughout the entire book,
hinting at it and alluding to it — but now he speaks it clearly. The
way to live life before God is to fear Him and obey Him. Look at
the other verses on fearing God and jot down your response to
each one.

3:14

God is all powerful forever

5:6-7

REMEMBER
The fear of the Lord is
the beginning of all
wisdom, knowledge,
and understanding.

8:13-14

judgement will come to the wicked

The fear of God has been a constant, recurring theme throughout The Poetical Books. Read the following verses: Job 1:1,8-9;
2:3; Psalm 33:6-9; 34:11-14; 111:10; Proverbs 1:7; 9:10; 31:30.
Although this is only a small sample of verses about the fear of
the Lord, what did you see in these verses that was helpful to you?

In the Preacher's portrait in Ecclesiastes 12:13, the fear of God
precedes the keeping of His commandments. This makes sense.
As we learn to worship God, we will want to walk with Him. As
we fall in love with Him, we will long to please Him. When we
sense His passion for holiness, we will want to live holy lives.

In Day Two of your study of Proverbs, you meditated on the
concept of fearing God. Review what you wrote that day and
write here what you have since learned about the fear of God.

*Man, made in the
image of God, has a
purpose — to be in
relationship to God,
who is there. Man
forgets his purpose and
thus he forgets who he
is and what life means.*

—FRANCIS A. SCHAEFFER,
theologian and writer

The Preacher's sermon is finished and his encouragement is clear: In a world filled with emptiness and futility, we can experience genuine enjoyment and pleasure only by fearing and obeying our God who is good, in control, and just.

Spend time meditating on these attributes of God and consider how He has demonstrated them to you.

I know nothing except what everyone knows — if there when grace dances, I should dance.

—W. H. AUDEN, poet

MEMORY VERSE

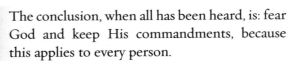 The conclusion, when all has been heard, is: fear God and keep His commandments, because this applies to every person.

ECCLESIASTES 12:13

ECCLESIASTES
[Life of Enjoyment]

REVIEW

1. The theme of Ecclesiastes is a life of genuine _enjoyment_ .

2. Chapter 1, our Crucial Chapter, introduces the concept of
"_vanity_ of vanities."

3. Our Notable Feature in the book is the Preacher's encouragement to
enjoy life to the fullest.

4. _God_ is our Prominent Player, and He is good, in control, and just.

5. "The conclusion, when all has been heard, is: _fear_ God and keep His commandments, because this applies to every person."

ECCLESIASTES 12:_____

SONG OF SOLOMON

[Marriage of Intimacy]

Many waters cannot quench love,

Nor will rivers overflow it;

If a man were to give all the riches of his house for love,

It would be utterly despised.

SONG OF SOLOMON 8:7

FIVE

SONG OF SOLOMON
[Marriage of Intimacy]

INTRODUCTION

The relationship between man and woman, husband and wife has been greatly challenged in the last century. Admiration for one another's differences has given way to competition, suspicion has replaced trust, and selfishness and pride have challenged respect. As a result of this, countless marriages have suffered. Yet here in The Poetical Books, God gives a ringing endorsement of marital love.

Song of Solomon is one of the most beautiful love poems ever written. It is a dramatic story, probably written by Solomon, that portrays the courtship, wedding, honeymoon, and marriage between one husband and his wife. This exquisite poem is filled with imagery and beauty as the lovers pour out words of affection and love for one another.

It is a book for today. It is a book for married lovers. It is a book of encouragement that reveals God's stamp of approval on sexual intimacy between a husband and wife, clearly portraying the joy, romance, challenge, and heartache of love in marriage.

SONG OF SOLOMON
[Marriage of Intimacy]

OVERVIEW

WHO: Author: Probably Solomon
Main Characters: King Solomon and his bride, the Shulammite

WHAT: Portrays a marriage of intimate love

WHEN: About 965 BC (Solomon's early years)

WHERE: Israel

WHY: A divine perspective on marriage

I. **THE PROBLEMS WITH SONG OF SOLOMON**

   A. There are no religious _themes_ .

   B. There are different _interpretions_ .

   1. Some Jews have interpreted it as an allegory about Israel and God.

   2. Some Christians have interpreted it as a typology of Christ and the church.

   3. It can be interpreted literally as a love relationship between man and woman.

II. **THE COURTSHIP OF SOLOMON AND THE SHULAMMITE (SONG OF SOLOMON 1:2–3:5)**

   A. They expressed their mutual _admiration_ for one another.

   B. God puts His stamp of approval on pleasure and passion in the love relationship.

   C. They both put _boundaries_ around their physical love until marriage.

III. **THE WEDDING AND HONEYMOON OF SOLOMON AND THE SHULAMMITE (SONG OF SOLOMON 3:6–5:1)**

   A. It was a military wedding.

B. The _____celebration_____ was joyful and extravagant.

C. They shared their _____hearts_____ (friendship) in courtship before they shared their bodies (lovers) in marriage.

D. The Shulammite invited her husband to _____enjoy_____ her physically.

E. He was _____satisfied_____, content, and joyful with her.

F. God placed His stamp of _____approval_____ upon their sexual love for one another.

IV. THE MARRIAGE OF SOLOMON AND THE SHULAMMITE (SONG OF SOLOMON 5:2–8:4)

A. Song of Solomon reveals that there are problems in marriage.

B. The Shulammite had become _____apathetic_____ toward her husband.

C. Solomon left the house.

  1. The Shulammite went after her husband to bring him back to her.

  2. He forgave her and received her back.

D. She invited him on a vacation so they could renew their love for one another.

V. THE CHARACTERISTICS OF THE SHULAMMITE: LESSONS FOR TODAY

A. She used kind words to praise her husband to others.

B. She was a woman of kind actions.

C. She was willing to humble herself and say she was sorry.

D. She was a woman of purity.

VI. CHRIST IS OUR TRUE BRIDEGROOM.

    A. Christ can cleanse.

    B. Christ can forgive.

APPLICATION

Man and wife are to enjoy one another, love one another, and cherish one another all the days of their lives.

SONG OF SOLOMON
[Marriage of Intimacy]

LEARNING FOR LIFE

1. Briefly review all of The Poetical Books.

2. What did you learn today about God's view of romance and intimacy in marriage?

3. What is the world's view of romance, sex, and marriage? How does it differ from God's view?

4. Who is the true Bridegroom, and who is His bride? (See Revelation 19:7.)

SONG OF SOLOMON
[Marriage of Intimacy]

DAY ONE

COMPLETE READ: Chapters 1:1–2:7
QUICK READ: Chapters 1:1–2:7

THE BIG PICTURE

The book is called the "best of songs," and understandably so. This is a song which Adam could have sung in Paradise when the Lord in His wise providence led Eve to him to be his wife. In frank but pure language the book praises the mutual love between husband and wife, and thereby teaches us not to despise physical beauty and married love as being of a low order.

—SIERD WOUDSTRA

Christianity has glorified marriage more than any other religion; and nearly all the greatest love poetry in the world has been produced by Christians.

—C. S. LEWIS

He is the half part of a blessed man, left to be finished by such as she, and she a fair divided excellence, whose fullness of perfection lies in him.

—WILLIAM SHAKESPEARE,
King John

The title of this book literally means "the most beautiful song" of Solomon, and evidently he wrote many. In a passage describing the incredible wisdom and breadth of the mind of Solomon (see 1 Kings 4:29-34), we are told that he wrote not only three thousand proverbs but also over one thousand songs.

Although there is some debate over the authorship of this book, strong arguments point to Solomon:

- His name is in the title in 1:1.

- He is mentioned by name in 1:5; 3:7,9,11; 8:11-12.

REMEMBER
Song of Solomon is a
biblical picture of
married love.

- He was knowledgeable about nature (see 1 Kings 4:33), which predominates the poetry of the book.

- The book mentions geographical locations appropriate to his time.

Many scholars believe Solomon wrote Ecclesiastes during his elderly years, Proverbs during his middle years, and Song of Solomon in his younger years. If so, the date of this writing would be approximately 965 BC.

No other book's interpretation has been more debated. Some believe it is chiefly an allegory of God's love for Israel. Others see the book as typology, a prefiguring of Christ as the Bridegroom and His church as the bride. There is no evidence within the book itself that suggests either of these approaches. C. S. Lewis once observed, "Almost everything can be read into any book if you are determined enough. Some of the allegories thus imposed on my books have been so ingenious and interesting that I after wished I had thought of them myself."[1]

A third interpretation, which we will follow in this study, is the literal approach: that the book is a song celebrating the love of a man and wife, from courtship through the wedding and into marriage. As such, it celebrates beauty and sexuality and posits a strong endorsement by God of physical and emotional intimacy within His divinely created institution of marriage. If you've read today's reading, you probably sensed that God intends marriage to be a setting for intimate love.

Jot down some words or phrases describing your thoughts as you read 1:1—2:7.

A lot of analogies

*Marriage is our last,
best chance to
grow up.*
—JOSEPH BARTH,
1745–1818

Poetry is not easily outlined or divided into sections for purposes of charting. The same is true of this most beautiful of songs. However, to better see the overall flow of these emotional lyrics, our readings for each day will follow this breakdown:

1:1–2:7	2:8–3:5	3:6–5:1	5:2–8:4	8:5-14
Expression of Their Mutual Admiration	Expression of Their Mutual Desires	Expression of Their Marital Consummation	Expression of Their Marital Adjustments	Expression of Their Mutual Love and Union
COURTSHIP		WEDDING	MARRIAGE	

This love story begins with King Solomon visiting one of his vineyards in the country of the Shulammite woman. She worked in the vineyard with her brother, and when Solomon saw her, he was smitten. Eventually, he won her heart and brought her back to his palace in Jerusalem as his bride. Song of Solomon allows us an intimate look into the lovers' physical and emotional relationship.

Remember that Song of Solomon is part of the wisdom literature of the Bible. When we studied Proverbs, we learned that wisdom means "skill in living." Ecclesiastes teaches us how to live skillfully in light of the futility of life "under the sun." Song of Solomon models skillful living in the most significant human relationship of life — marriage.

All women, whether single, married, divorced, or widowed, can benefit from this study. Ask God to help you determine the purpose and benefits of a study of Song of Solomon in your present circumstance. Take some time now to talk with Him about His desire for you in your study this week.

Two souls fused into one by an impassioned love — friends, counselors — a mutual support and inspiration to each other amid life's struggles; this is marriage.
— ELIZABETH CADY STANTON, women's rights advocate

MEMORY VERSE

Many waters cannot quench love,
Nor will rivers overflow it;
If a man were to give all the riches of his house for love,
It would be utterly despised.

SONG OF SOLOMON 8:7

REVIEW IT!
The theme of Song of Solomon is a marriage of intimate love.

Song of Solomon
[Marriage of Intimacy]

REMEMBER
Song of Solomon is a
duet, not a solo.

DAY TWO

COMPLETE READ: Chapters 2:8–3:5
QUICK READ: Chapters 2:8–3:5

NOTABLE FEATURE NUMBER I

The Song of Solomon is a notable example of how one love poet solved the problem of depicting romantic, sexual love in literature. On the one hand the poet avoids the pitfall of allowing the love to evaporate into an abstraction by continually making physical attractiveness the main ingredient of the romantic relationship.

—LELAND RYKEN

*I understand thy kisses,
and thou mine.*

—WILLIAM SHAKESPEARE,
Henry IV

The Song of Songs is a book of love—sexual, erotic love. It is not written to tell about that love; it celebrates it. In language which is allusive but very specific, the book expresses the enjoyment of physical passion.

—WESLEY J. FUERST

Sensuous love with erotic overtones is God's intent for the marriage relationship. The distortion of that relationship has no doubt abased this dimension of life, but that does not justify placing such experience — or Scripture's Song about it — into the inactive file of living.

—HOWARD G. HENDRICKS

According to these writers, Song of Solomon celebrates romantic, sexual, erotic, and passionate love. This is our first Notable Feature — that marital love as God intended includes all these facets.

The bridegroom's lengthiest expression of his love for his bride is found in 4:1-15. Even though you may not understand all the terminology, read this passage and respond to the following questions.

What parts of his bride's body did the bridegroom praise?

eyes, hair, teeth, lips mouth temples, neck, breast

DID YOU KNOW?
The phrase *whom my soul loves* is used five times in the book.

Write down the descriptions that are most striking to you.

How do you think his bride responded to such praise?

In chapter 5, the roles are reversed. In verse 8 the bride said she was lovesick, and in response, the chorus (a common device of lyrical literature) asked her to describe the one she loved. Read her description in 5:10-16 and write your response to the following questions.

What parts of her bridegroom's body did the bride describe?

head, hair eyes, cheeks, lips arms, body, legs

From her description, how do you believe she felt about him?

enamored

Oh to be able to celebrate you with all the words of joy.
—PABLO NERUDA, Spanish poet

What a happy and holy fashion it is that those who love one another should rest on the same pillow.

—Nathaniel Hawthorne, in a love letter to Sophia Peabody, his future wife, 1839

Do you think this description would please her lover?

Based on these two passages, what principles can you discern that would enhance a married couple's physical and emotional love for each other?

Spiritual

Pray as God leads in response to what you've read in His Word.

REVIEW IT!
Our first Notable Feature is that God intended marital love to be romantic, sexual, erotic, and passionate.

MEMORY VERSE

Many waters cannot quench love,
Nor will rivers overflow it;
If a man were to give all the riches of his house for love,
It would be utterly despised.

SONG OF SOLOMON 8:7

SONG OF SOLOMON
[Marriage of Intimacy]

DAY THREE

COMPLETE READ: Chapters 3:6—5:1
QUICK READ: Chapters 3:6—5:1

NOTABLE FEATURE NUMBER 2

Chuck Swindoll, in his book *Strike the Original Match*, tells this story:

Four-year-old Suzie had just been told the story of "Snow White" for the first time in her life. She could hardly wait to get home from nursery school to tell her mommy. With wide-eyed excitement, she retold the fairy tale to her mother that afternoon. After relating how Prince Charming had arrived on his beautiful white horse and kissed Snow White back to life, Suzie asked loudly:

"And do you know what happened then?"

"Yes," said her mom, "they lived happily ever after."

"No," responded Suzie, with a frown, ". . . they got married."[2]

In her childlike innocence, that little nursery schooler spoke the truth without realizing it. Getting married and living happily ever after are not necessarily synonymous.

Differences arise, daily stresses take their toll — marriage can be just plain hard! Our two lovers in the Song of Solomon are no different. But how they handle this facet of their marriage is our second Notable Feature of the book. The dictionary defines *gracious* as "kind; merciful or compassionate; disposed to show grace, favor."[3] The Song of Solomon shows us that graciousness in marriage is a healthy and helpful attitude when differences and misunderstandings arise.

Weddings have less to do with being married than with the fact that it is best to begin the most arduous journeys surrounded by friends and wearing nice clothes.

—TONY EARLEY, professor and short story author

The courtship of Solomon and the Shulammite was filled with anticipation and rich expressions of love. Their wedding was all they had dreamed — maybe even more. Finally, they were married. Read 5:2-8 and describe in your own words the incident that took place.

Evidently, Solomon's bride displayed a passive apathy to his late-night advances. We are unaware of the reason for his late arrival, but what often happens in marriage happened here — they just "missed" each other. He had a certain expectation, but she responded indifferently. Who was in the wrong? Maybe both of them. But regardless, they found themselves in a marital predicament. So he left and went back to work. On Day Two, you read his romantically stirring description of her in 4:1-15. The scene of her indifference is placed in the very next chapter — possibly to teach a major lesson about enduring intimate love. How will he respond the next time we see them together? We do not have long to wait. Read 6:4-13 and respond to the following questions.

Summarize his description of her in these verses.

Devoted

In a perfect union the man and woman are like a strung bow. Who is to say whether the string bends the bow, or the bow tightens the string?

—CYRIL CONNOLLY, critic and editor

Does it seem any less intense than in chapter 4?

No

Solomon was able to respond with grace and acceptance rather than taking offense, withdrawing, or casting blame. Some scholars believe 6:11 shows us that Solomon realized there was a problem needing to be addressed and told the Shulammite where he went — back to work — as a kind of confession.

The marriage relationship (or any relationship, for that matter) can be "ideal" for a time, but it will eventually become "real." And doesn't reality bring challenges, adjustments, and a need for regarding the other person as more important than yourself? Do you have a relationship, marital or otherwise, in which you have difficulty responding with graciousness when things don't go your way? If so, describe your struggle.

He that cannot forgive others breaks the bridge over which he must pass himself; for every man has need to be forgiven.

—THOMAS FULLER,
English clergyman

In light of this struggle, what would be a proper response for you right now?

MEMORY VERSE

Many waters cannot quench love,
Nor will rivers overflow it;
If a man were to give all the riches of his house for love,
It would be utterly despised.

SONG OF SOLOMON 8:7

REVIEW IT!
Our second Notable Feature is the importance of graciousness (kindness, compassion, showing mercy) when marriage becomes difficult.

SONG OF SOLOMON
[Marriage of Intimacy]

SONG OF SOLOMON
[Marriage of Intimacy]

AMAZING!
All together there are 172 references to nature in just 8 chapters!

DAY FOUR

COMPLETE READ: Chapters 5:2–8:4
QUICK READ: Chapters 5:2–8:4

NOTABLE FEATURE NUMBER 3

No artist could have fashioned two people better suited for one another. He was the king of their great nation; she, his chosen bride. Spring had seen their love blossom like the flowers in the palace gardens. Their love had been the talk of the court. It was destined to be a song for the world. For their romance was a romance for all seasons, indeed, for all centuries. And, in fact, so ideal was their love that the song about them was chosen as one of the books of sacred Scripture. It became the only one of the entire collection devoted exclusively to courtship and marriage.

—S. CRAIG GLICKMAN

Love seeks one thing only: the good of the one loved. It leaves all the other secondary effects to take care of themselves. Love, therefore, is its own reward.

—THOMAS MERTON, Catholic priest

You've probably heard the shallow clichés:

Love is like the measles; we all have to go through it.

Love is what makes the world go 'round.

Love is a warm puppy.

Love is a many-splendored thing.

Love is never having to say you're sorry.

AMAZING!
All together there are 172 references to nature in just 8 chapters!

COMPLETE READ: Chapters 5:2–8:4
QUICK READ: Chapters 5:2–8:4

NOTABLE FEATURE NUMBER 3

No artist could have fashioned two people better suited for one another. He was the king of their great nation; she, his chosen bride. Spring had seen their love blossom like the flowers in the palace gardens. Their love had been the talk of the court. It was destined to be a song for the world. For their romance was a romance for all seasons, indeed, for all centuries. And, in fact, so ideal was their love that the song about them was chosen as one of the books of sacred Scripture. It became the only one of the entire collection devoted exclusively to courtship and marriage.

—S. CRAIG GLICKMAN

Love seeks one thing only: the good of the one loved. It leaves all the other secondary effects to take care of themselves. Love, therefore, is its own reward.

—THOMAS MERTON, Catholic priest

You've probably heard the shallow clichés:

Love is like the measles; we all have to go through it.

Love is what makes the world go 'round.

Love is a warm puppy.

Love is a many-splendored thing.

Love is never having to say you're sorry.

x

134   SONG OF SOLOMON: DAY FOUR

The Song of Solomon, God's love poem for a husband and wife, does not portray "love in the shallows." Though it doesn't give the complete biblical picture of love, it does set an incredibly high standard for married lovers — nothing less than a complete giving of oneself to the other.

This is our third Notable Feature — that the Song of Solomon portrays a rich and multifaceted marital love. We see pictures of this throughout the book. Besides the individual expressions of love the bride and bridegroom share with each other, we also find vivid descriptions of love.

After each of the following statements, record your thoughts on its meaning and significance.

For your love is better than wine (1:2; 4:10).

He has brought me to his banquet hall, and his banner over me is love (2:4).

How beautiful is your love, my sister, my bride (4:10)!

For love is as strong as death (8:6).

Only love can bring individual beings to their perfect completion as individuals, because only love takes possession of them and unites them by what lies deepest within them.

—PIERRE TEILHARD DE CHARDIN, geologist and paleontologist

Many waters cannot quench love, nor will rivers overflow it (8:7).

If a man were to give all the riches of his house for love, it would be utterly despised (8:7).

Combine your thoughts from these brief depictions of love with the more extended and explicit expressions you have read throughout this study. Write a summary description of love as it is portrayed in the Song of Solomon.

Whatever your marital status, what does this book tell you about God's original idea for love?

REVIEW IT!
Our third Notable Feature is the book's portrait of marital love as rich and multifaceted.

MEMORY VERSE

Many waters cannot quench love,
Nor will rivers overflow it;
If a man were to give all the riches of his house for love,
It would be utterly despised.

SONG OF SOLOMON 8:7

SONG OF SOLOMON
[Marriage of Intimacy]

DAY FIVE

COMPLETE READ: Chapter 8:5-14
QUICK READ: Chapter 8:5-14

COUNT 'EM
In Song of Solomon,
there are thirty-seven
references to nature
apart from animals,
plants, and minerals.

A TIMELESS PRINCIPLE

What I needed most was to love and to be loved.
—SAINT AUGUSTINE OF HIPPO

There's a good reason why we desire more than anything else to be known and cherished and loved. We were *created* to be loved. God formed our hearts to be loved by those with whom we share our lives. And when we are so loved, it feels wonderful. But that's not always how it works out.

Sally wants to be married. But at thirty-seven, she is beginning to believe she will never find the man with whom she longs to make a life. Lisa had a great marriage — or so she thought — until her husband walked out of her life and into the arms of another woman. Susan, a widow for two years now, still faces each day with an ache and a loneliness she never could have imagined. Katherine, married for fifteen years, is about to give up once and for all her dreams of "happily ever after." Her marriage isn't a place of passion or joy. All she feels is confusion, disappointment, and the drudgery of making it through another day.

The LORD is near to the brokenhearted and saves those who are crushed in spirit.
—Psalm 34:18

There's nothing like the Song of Solomon, with its celebration of married love, to remind these women — and maybe you — of the heartache life often deals us in the area of relationships — heartache that leaves us feeling anything but loved.

And yet we *are* loved. In fact, the One who shaped our very hearts is the One who loves us more perfectly and completely than anyone else. Is it truly possible to find and know and *feel* love from the One who loves us most? Even when our hearts are broken?

Writer and priest Henri Nouwen knew this rare attainment. Devoted to a life of celibacy and serving others — even the severely mentally and physically handicapped — he battled loneliness for years, despairing of ever feeling truly loved. Plunging at times into deep depression, he struggled to believe that God could love him in a way that was tangible and real. Through this dark time and with the help of devoted spiritual directors, Nouwen began to sense the love of God in a way he had never before known.

His book *The Inner Voice of Love* is Nouwen's private journal from this dark, yet redemptive time. In it he recorded not only his thoughts and struggles but also the encouragement and direction of his spiritual mentors. He writes in his journal (addressing himself),

> Right now you feel nothing except emptiness and the lack of strength to choose. But keep saying, "God loves me, and God's love is enough." You have to choose the solid place over and over again and return to it after every failure. . . .
>
> You sense that nothing but God's love can fulfill your deepest need while the pull to other people and things remains strong. . . .
>
> You feel a strange sadness. An enormous loneliness emerges, but you are not frightened. You feel vulnerable but safe at the same time. Jesus is where you are, and you can trust that He will show you the next step.[4]

Has there been a time in your life when you felt abandoned and empty? If so, when was it and what was the situation?

Blessed be the LORD, Because He has heard the voice of my supplication. The LORD is my strength and my shield; my heart trusts in Him, and I am helped.

—Psalm 28:6-7

The prophet Jeremiah experienced rejection and loneliness and knew what it meant to feel forsaken. He believed God could have stepped in and saved him from all his pain, so he vented his despair and anger directly to God. Read Lamentations 3:1-32. What happened to Jeremiah when he remembered God's lovingkindness?

Even when we aren't in such desperate circumstances, we can easily forget God's faithful love for us. Spend some time remembering God's lovingkindness by reading Psalm 71 (aloud if your circumstances permit) as a prayer. Underline a few phrases that remind you of God's faithful love.

Over time, Henri Nouwen was able, like Jeremiah, to remember God's faithful love. Nearly a decade after his dark journey and just a few years before his death, he wrote these words:

> I have moved through anguish to freedom, through depression to peace, through despair to hope.... What once seemed such a curse has become a blessing. All the agony that threatened to destroy my life now seems like the fertile ground for greater trust, stronger hope, and deeper love.... I now know that while I felt completely abandoned, God didn't leave me alone.[5]

MEMORY VERSE

Many waters cannot quench love,
Nor will rivers overflow it;
If a man were to give all the riches of his house for love,
It would be utterly despised.

SONG OF SOLOMON 8:7

God, the great holy Lord God, thinks of you, notices you, regards you, sets His heart upon you. His thoughts cluster around you, clinging to you with a grasp so fervent and intense as though He were solely and supremely absorbed with you and your concerns. . . . There is not a moment that He is not thinking of you.
—OCTAVIUS WINSLOW, British pastor

SONG OF SOLOMON
[Marriage of Intimacy]

REVIEW

1. The theme of Song of Solomon is a marriage of _____intimate_____ love.

2. Our first Notable Feature is that God intended _____marital_____ love to be romantic, sexual, erotic, and passionate.

3. Our second Notable Feature is the importance of _____graciousness_____ (kindness, compassion, showing mercy) when marriage becomes difficult.

4. Our third Notable Feature is the book's portrait of marital love as rich and _____multifaceted_____.

5. "Many waters cannot _____quench_____ love,
   Nor will rivers overflow it;
   If a man were to give all the riches of his house for love,
   It would be utterly despised."

   SONG OF SOLOMON 8:__7__

COMPREHENSIVE REVIEW OF
THE POETICAL BOOKS

JOB

1. The theme of Job is the suffering of man and the

   _____ of God.

2. The Prominent Player in the book is _____ .

3. Chapter 42 is our Crucial Chapter because Job repented and God

   _____ him.

4. Our Notable Feature is the book's description of God's sovereignty over all

   _____ .

5. "Naked I came from my mother's womb

   And naked I shall return there.

   The LORD gave and the LORD has taken away.

   _____ be the name of the LORD."

   JOB 1:_____

PSALMS

1. The theme of Psalms is a life of _____ worship.

2. Psalm 1 is our Crucial Chapter because it _____ the book
   of Psalms so effectively.

3. _____ is our Prominent Player because he wrote more of
   the psalms than any other person.

4. A Notable Feature of the book of Psalms is that it clearly models the importance of
   sharing our most _____ thoughts and feelings with God.

5. "One thing I have asked from the LORD, that I shall seek:

That I may dwell in the house of the LORD all the days of my life,

To _____ the beauty of the LORD

And to meditate in His temple."

PSALM 27:_____

PROVERBS

1. The theme of Proverbs is a life of _____ living.

2. Chapter 1 is a Crucial Chapter because it spells out the _____ of the book, introduces us to the four main characters of the book, and gives us the book's motto.

3. _____ , our Prominent Player and the author of Proverbs, failed at times to apply his own wisdom.

4. Our Notable Feature is the description of the _____ woman who fears God in Proverbs 31.

5. "The fear of the LORD is the beginning of _____ , And the knowledge of the Holy One is understanding."

PROVERBS 9:_____

ECCLESIASTES

1. The theme of Ecclesiastes is a life of genuine _____ .

2. Chapter 1, our Crucial Chapter, introduces the concept of
" _____ of vanities."

3. Our Notable Feature in the book is the Preacher's encouragement to _____ life to the fullest.

4. _____ is our Prominent Player, and He is good, in control, and just.

5. "The conclusion, when all has been heard, is: _____ God and keep His commandments, because this applies to every person."

Ecclesiastes 12:_____

Song of Solomon

1. The theme of Song of Solomon is a marriage of _____ love.

2. Our first Notable Feature is that God intended _____ love to be romantic, sexual, erotic, and passionate.

3. Our second Notable Feature is the importance of _____ (kindness, compassion, showing mercy) when marriage becomes difficult.

4. Our third Notable Feature is the book's portrait of marital love as rich and

   _____ .

5. "Many waters cannot _____ love,
   Nor will rivers overflow it;
   If a man were to give all the riches of his house for love,
   It would be utterly despised."

Song of Solomon 8:_____

CONGRATULATIONS!

You have just completed The Poetical Books, and we hope you have experienced a deep, reverential awe of your God. He is all-wise, as seen in Proverbs and Ecclesiastes, sovereign in Job, full of beauty and majesty in Psalms, and our beloved Bridegroom in Song of Solomon.

Now our adventure takes us to the fifth set, The Major Prophets. These books are the first in a series of seventeen prophetical books. The five major prophets are called "major" because most of them are longer in nature than the other twelve.

The scene for these books is a somber one. As Judah was sinking deep into depravity, God did not stand by and do nothing. Over and over He sent prophets to speak His words, encouraging His people to repent and be restored to right fellowship with Him. He is like a Father calling to a wayward son He loves, begging him to turn back from the path of destruction. He is also a Judge, warning that destruction is sure if repentance does not come. Many of the prophecies in these books have come true just as they were written; others are yet to be fulfilled.

Each prophet had a significant message, and although these books are not widely read today, their messages are still important for us. God is our Father God — but He is also the righteous Judge of mankind, and He is unchanging. As you move on to set five, read each page to discover the great character of God who warns and warns and warns until He sends discipline. He is long-suffering. He is merciful. And it is His great love that will bring about discipline.

So let the adventure continue as we move on to set five of *The Amazing Collection: The Bible for Women, Book by Book.*

CHRONOLOGICAL RELATIONSHIP OF THE OLD TESTAMENT BOOKS

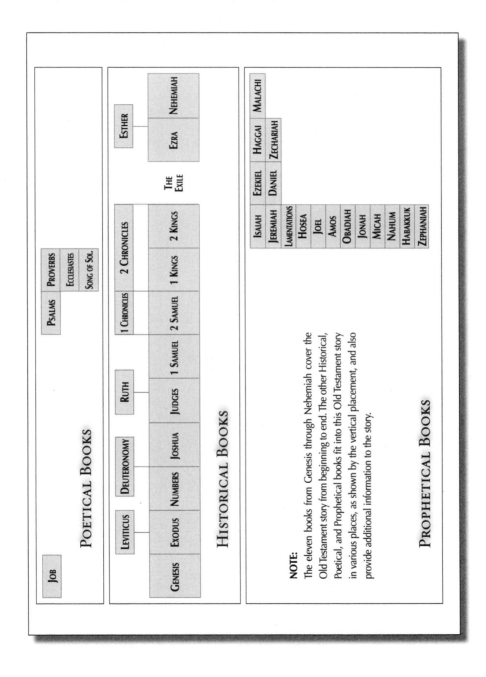

POETICAL BOOKS

JOB

PSALMS | PROVERBS / ECCLESIASTES / SONG OF SOL.

HISTORICAL BOOKS

GENESIS | EXODUS | LEVITICUS | NUMBERS | DEUTERONOMY | JOSHUA | JUDGES | RUTH | 1 SAMUEL | 2 SAMUEL | 1 CHRONICLES | 1 KINGS | 2 CHRONICLES | 2 KINGS | THE EXILE | ESTHER | EZRA | NEHEMIAH

PROPHETICAL BOOKS

ISAIAH | JEREMIAH | LAMENTATIONS | HOSEA | JOEL | AMOS | OBADIAH | JONAH | MICAH | NAHUM | HABAKKUK | ZEPHANIAH | EZEKIEL | DANIEL | HAGGAI | ZECHARIAH | MALACHI

NOTE:

The eleven books from Genesis through Nehemiah cover the Old Testament story from beginning to end. The other Historical, Poetical, and Prophetical books fit into this Old Testament story in various places, as shown by the vertical placement, and also provide additional information to the story.

ANSWER KEY TO OUTLINES

Job

I. CONTROVERSY: IN HEAVEN BETWEEN GOD AND SATAN

    A. God's wager before Satan: "Have you considered my servant <u>JOB</u>?"

        1. Satan argued that Job was righteous because God gave him <u>EVERYTHING</u>.

        2. Satan was given permission to take away Job's wealth.

            a. Satan took away all of Job's <u>POSSESSIONS</u>.

            b. Satan took away Job's <u>CHILDREN</u>.

        3. Job's response: "Naked I came from my mother's womb,
            And naked I shall return there.
            The LORD gave and the LORD has taken away.
            Blessed be the name of the LORD." (Job 1:21)

        4. Satan was given permission to take away Job's health.

            a. Job was covered with <u>BOILS</u> from head to foot.

            b. He suffered severe depression.

II. CONTROVERSY: ON EARTH BETWEEN JOB AND HIS FRIENDS

    A. Friends came to comfort Job because of his suffering.

        1. They <u>WEPT</u> over the suffering of Job.

        2. They sat in silence for <u>SEVEN</u> days.

    B. Friends confronted Job that his suffering must be because he had sinned.

        1. Eliphaz argued from <u>EXPERIENCE</u>.

2. Bildad argued from <u>TRADITION</u>.

3. Zophar argued from <u>COMMON SENSE</u>.

   a. First cycle was general: mild <u>SUGGESTION</u>.

   b. Second cycle was specific: <u>CONDEMNATION</u>.

   c. Third cycle was very specific: <u>HARSH</u> reproof.

C. Job became more <u>SELF-</u> focused (Job 29).

D. Job called God into the <u>COURTROOM</u> (Job 23:3-7).

E. Elihu, the youngest, argued from <u>WISDOM</u>.

III.   CONTROVERSY: ON EARTH BETWEEN GOD AND JOB

   A. God spoke to Job from a <u>WHIRLWIND</u> (Job 38).

   B. Through a series of questions God revealed His <u>WISDOM</u>.

    1. Job acknowledged his insignificance.

    2. Job responded with <u>SILENCE</u>.

   C. God revealed His <u>POWER</u>.

    1. Job acknowledged God's sovereignty.

    2. Job <u>REPENTED</u>.

   D. God blessed Job with twice as many possessions.

PSALMS

I.   THE FIVE PARTS OF PSALMS

   A. Book 1 relates to <u>MAN</u> (Psalms 1–41).

   B. Book 2 relates to the <u>NATION</u> (Psalms 42–72).

   C. Book 3 relates to the <u>SANCTUARY</u> (Psalms 73–89).

   D. Book 4 relates to the <u>EARTH</u> (Psalms 90–106).

   E. Book 5 relates to the <u>WORD OF GOD</u> (Psalms 107–150).

II. THE FINER POINTS OF PSALMS

A. Psalms gives us many descriptions of who God is and are known as God's character or <u>ATTRIBUTES</u>.

B. Psalms encourages us with words of <u>HOPE</u> and <u>COMFORT</u>.

C. Psalms contains personal prayers of admission of sin called <u>CONFESSION</u>.

D. Psalms is a heartfelt collection of truthful feelings (both good and bad) and is, therefore, considered a book of <u>HONESTY</u>.

E. Psalms contains much <u>INSTRUCTION</u> on how to live a righteous life.

F. Psalms is full of <u>PROPHECY</u> describing future events, especially regarding the life and death of the promised Messiah.

G. Psalms is considered a book of <u>THANKSGIVING</u> and calls on us to be grateful for all blessings.

PROVERBS

I. PROVERBS FOR YOUTH (PROVERBS 1–9)

A. The main purpose of Proverbs is found in verses 1:1-6.

1. <u>WISDOM</u> — living life skillfully

2. To know <u>INSTRUCTION</u> — training usually under pressure, discipline

3. <u>UNDERSTANDING</u> — insight, ability to discern good from evil

4. <u>WISE BEHAVIOR</u> — common sense in circumstances

5. To give <u>PRUDENCE</u>—discretion, foresight, watchfulness, shrewdness

6. To the youth <u>KNOWLEDGE</u>—factual information, truth, principles

7. And <u>DISCRETION</u>—meditation, clear and able thinking

B. The motto of the book of Proverbs is found in verse 1:7: "The <u>FEAR</u> of the Lord. . . ."

C. The main focus is on parent/child training (Proverbs 1:8–7:27).

1. The main form of poetry in this first section is the instructional <u>SONNET</u>.

2. Most of these thematic sonnets begin with the phrase, "MY SON. . . ."

3. The four main characters in the sonnets are the naive, the fool, the scoffers, and the WISE man.

D. The main character in the monologues is WISDOM personified (Proverbs 8–9).

II. PROVERBS OF SOLOMON (PROVERBS 10–24)

A. There are three main types of parallelisms found in the Proverbs:

1. Contrastive parallelisms — where opposite thoughts are put together. They are signified by the word "BUT."

2. Completive parallelisms — the first line agrees with the second line. They usually have the word "AND" between the first and the second sentences.

3. Comparative parallelisms — compare godliness with ungodliness. They often have the word "THAN" helping the sentence to agree.

B. There are two types of analogy and imagery found in the Proverbs:

1. Epigrams — short, WITTY statements or sayings

2. Aphorisms — short, WISE statements or sayings

III. PROVERBS COMPILED BY HEZEKIAH (PROVERBS 25–31)

A. The Thirteen SAYINGS of Agur (Proverbs 30)

1. Agur was thought to be an Ishmaelite.

2. Agur's sayings were verbally communicated and rhetorical in nature.

3. Agur reminded the listener that only God is wise.

B. The ORACLE of Lemuel (Proverbs 31:1-9)

1. Lemuel was believed to be an Arabian king.

2. Lemuel's mother gave him this wise advice verbally.

3. Lemuel's charge was for leaders.

C. The ACROSTIC of the Wise Woman (Proverbs 31:10-31)

1. An acrostic is a written poem or series of lines, in which certain letters form a motto, message, or sequence.

2. This acrostic has twenty-two verses where the first letter of each verse consecutively follows the complete Hebrew alphabet.

3. This acrostic portrays the virtuous wife.

ECCLESIASTES

I. THE PROBLEM: LIFE WITHOUT GOD IS MEANINGLESS (ECCLESIASTES 1–6)

A. Solomon sought meaning in:

1. WISDOM — He excelled in science and knowledge.

2. WINE — He tried all pleasure and laughter.

3. WORKS — He achieved great accomplishments and business success.

4. WEALTH — He accumulated possessions including gold and servants.

5. WOMEN — He enjoyed the pleasure of men.

Conclusion: He hated life because everything is futile (Ecclesiastes 2:17).

B. Solomon saw emptiness in:

1. REALITY — We're in time ending in death, but eternity is in our heart.

2. RELATIONSHIPS — We oppress others, compete, and are unfaithful.

3. RELIGION — We make empty prayers and vows.

4. RICHES — We die and leave our riches or lose them.

II. THE SOLUTION: LIFE WITH GOD IS MEANINGFUL (ECCLESIASTES 7–12)

A. God gives life meaning.

1. God is in CONTROL—man is not!

2. God knows the FUTURE—man does not!

3. God gives ENJOYMENT—things and pleasures do not.

a. We are to enjoy our <u>WORK</u>—for it is God's gift.

b. We are to enjoy our <u>WEALTH</u>—it too is God's gift.

c. We are to enjoy our <u>WIFE</u> (husband) — for this is our reward.

B. God gives death meaning.

1. Death is going to our eternal <u>HOME</u> (Ecclesiastes 12:5).

2. At death our body returns to the earth but our spirit returns to <u>GOD</u> (Ecclesiastes 12:7).

SONG OF SOLOMON

I. THE PROBLEMS WITH SONG OF SOLOMON

A. There are no religious <u>THEMES</u>.

B. There are different <u>INTERPRETATIONS</u>.

1. Some Jews have interpreted it as an allegory about Israel and God.

2. Some Christians have interpreted it as a typology of Christ and the church.

3. It can be interpreted literally as a love relationship between man and woman.

II. THE COURTSHIP OF SOLOMON AND THE SHULAMMITE (SONG OF SOLOMON 1:2–3:5)

A. They expressed their mutual <u>ADMIRATION</u> for one another.

B. God puts His stamp of approval on pleasure and passion in the love relationship.

C. They both put <u>BOUNDARIES</u> around their physical love until marriage.

III. THE WEDDING AND HONEYMOON OF SOLOMON AND THE SHULAMMITE (SONG OF SOLOMON 3:6–5:1)

A. It was a military wedding.

B. The <u>CELEBRATION</u> was joyful and extravagant.

C. They shared their <u>HEARTS</u> (friendship) in courtship before they shared their bodies (lovers) in marriage.

D. The Shulammite invited her husband to <u>ENJOY</u> her physically.

E. He was <u>SATISFIED</u>, content, and joyful with her.

F. God placed His stamp of <u>APPROVAL</u> upon their sexual love for one another.

IV. THE MARRIAGE OF SOLOMON AND THE SHULAMMITE (SONG OF SOLOMON 5:2–8:4)

A. Song of Solomon reveals that there are problems in marriage.

B. The Shulammite had become <u>APATHETIC</u> toward her husband.

C. Solomon left the house.

    1. The Shulammite went after her husband to bring him back to her.

    2. He forgave her and received her back.

D. She invited him on a vacation so they could renew their love for one another.

V. THE CHARACTERISTICS OF THE SHULAMMITE: LESSONS FOR TODAY

A. She used kind words to praise her husband to others.

B. She was a woman of kind actions.

C. She was willing to humble herself and say she was sorry.

D. She was a woman of purity.

VI. CHRIST IS OUR TRUE BRIDEGROOM.

A. Christ can cleanse.

B. Christ can forgive.

NOTES

JOB

1. Philip Yancey, *The Bible Jesus Read* (Grand Rapids, Mich.: Zondervan, 1999), p. 63.

2. C. S. Lewis quoted in Yancey, p. 65.

3. J. I. Packer, *Knowing God* (Downers Grove, Ill.: InterVarsity, 1973), p. 13.

4. A. W. Tozer, *The Knowledge of the Holy* (New York: Harper & Row, 1961), p. 9.

5. Kenneth W. Osbech, *101 Hymn Stories* (Grand Rapids, Mich.: Kregel, 1982), pp. 126-127 and Alfred B. Smith, *Hymn Histories* (1981), pp. 25-26.

6. Horatio Spafford, "It Is Well with My Soul," *Hymns for the Family of God* (Nashville: Paragon Associates, Inc., 1976), p. 495.

PSALMS

1. Philip Yancey, *The Bible Jesus Read* (Grand Rapids, Mich.: Zondervan, 1999), p. 163.

2. Kathleen Norris quoted in Yancey, p. 113.

3. Yancey, pp. 122-123.

4. Eugene Peterson quoted in Yancey, p. 127.

PROVERBS

1. Leslie B. Flynn quoted in Alice Gray, *Stories for the Heart* (Sisters, Oreg.: Multnomah, 1996), p. 63.

2. Jan Meyers, *The Allure of Hope* (Colorado Springs, Colo.: NavPress, 2001), p. 46.

3. David Seamands quoted in Alice Gray, *More Stories for the Heart* (Sisters, Oreg.: Multnomah, 1996), p. 93.

4. Gray, *Stories for the Heart*, p. 88.

ECCLESIASTES

1. Saint Augustine quoted in A. Norman Jeffares and Martin Gray, *A Dictionary of Quotations* (New York: Barnes & Noble Books, 1997), p. 31.

2. Kenneth Hare quoted in J. I. Packer, *A Quest for Godliness* (Wheaton, Ill.: Crossway, 1990), p. 259.

3. H. L. Mencken quoted in A. Norman Jeffares and Martin Gray, p. 448.

SONG OF SOLOMON

1. C. S. Lewis quoted in "Bible Book of the Month," *Christianity Today*, April 27, 1959.

2. Charles R. Swindoll, *Strike the Original Match* (Sisters, Oreg.: Multnomah, 1980), p. 39.

3. Noah Webster, *American Dictionary of the English Language*, vol. 1, rev. ed. (San Francisco: Foundation for American Christian Education, reprint of 1828 edition, 1967), p. 93.

4. Henri J. Nouwen, *The Inner Voice of Love* (New York: Doubleday, 1996), pp. 8, 16, 18.

5. Nouwen, pp. 116-118.

LEADER'S GUIDE

1. *Webster's New Collegiate Dictionary* (Springfield, Mass.: G&C Merriam Co. Publishers, 1960), p. 237.

2. John K. Brilhart, *Effective Group Discussion* (Dubuque, Iowa: Wm. C. Brown Company Publishers, 1967), p. 26.

3. *How to Lead Small Group Bible Studies* (Colorado Springs, Colo.: NavPress, 1982), pp. 40-42.

BIOGRAPHIES

PAT HARLEY
Teacher

Pat committed her life to Jesus Christ at the age of thirty-two after He powerfully intervened and healed her broken marriage. After eight years of study, she began teaching the Bible to women, convinced that it is the Word of God that offers help and hope for women today. She is the founder and president of Big Dream Ministries, Inc. and served for eighteen years as the director of The Women's Fellowship, a former ministry to over five hundred women. She also served as the director of women's ministries at Fellowship Bible Church in Roswell, Georgia. Pat has a master of arts degree in education from Western Michigan University and has taken courses at Dallas Theological Seminary. She and her husband have two married daughters and several grandchildren.

ELEANOR LEWIS
Teacher

At the age of twenty-six, Eleanor accepted Christ for assurance of heaven. However, when her son was born with a severe birth defect, she turned to God's Word for answers and found not only a Savior but an all-powerful Lord. The Word of God came alive for her, and she began teaching and speaking at Christian women's clubs. For almost thirty years, she has taught Bible studies in churches, homes, and offices. In addition, she speaks at conferences and retreats across the country and internationally. She is president of Insights and Beginnings, Inc., which produced a video series and Bible study to help people understand their temperament types, overcome weaknesses, and use their strengths for the glory of God. Eleanor and her husband live in the Atlanta area and have a married son and one grandchild.

MARGIE RUETHER
Teacher

Though Margie was not raised in a churchgoing home, her parents committed their lives to Christ after Margie was in college. It was her mother's godly example and prayers that brought Margie to the throne of grace. Her growing love for Jesus and His Word led her to Bible Study Fellowship International, an interdenominational Christian organization in which laypeople teach Bible studies. After many years of study, she became a Substitute Teaching Leader and a member of the area team. She served there for a number of years before becoming one of the lead teachers at The Women's Fellowship in Roswell, Georgia. She has also facilitated a Bible teacher-training program for women and speaks at retreats and church conferences. She and her family live in Delaware.

LINDA SWEENEY
Teacher

Linda accepted Christ as her personal Savior when she was twelve years old. As an adult, she grew to love God's Word more and more. She began to see God change not only her life but the lives of others when they adhere to the wisdom of Scripture. Because of her passion to excite women to know the Word and to see their lives change as they respond in obedience, she began teaching the Bible to women in her church and community under God's leading. She has taught Sunday school for many years and was a much-loved Bible Study Fellowship International Teaching Leader for eight years. During that time, she not only taught hundreds of women weekly but also trained a large group of Bible Study Fellowship International leaders in her class. She has taught women's retreats and spoken at women's meetings and conferences throughout the South. She and her husband live in the Atlanta area and have a married daughter, a son, and two grandchildren.

ART VANDER VEEN
Senior Copywriter

Art began his relationship with Christ at age thirteen. In his late twenties after graduating from the University of New Mexico, he began preparing for full-time ministry. He earned a Th.M. degree from Dallas Theological Seminary and has ministered on the staff of Campus Crusade for Christ. He was one of the original team members of Walk Thru the Bible Ministries and served as chaplain for the Atlanta Falcons. In 1979, he was part of a team that founded Fellowship Bible Church in Roswell, Georgia, where he was a pastor for nearly twenty-five years. He now serves as pastor, teacher, and mentor at Little Branch Community Church in the Atlanta area. Art is passionate about helping people understand the Scriptures as the revealed truth from and about God. He and his wife, Jan, have three married children and seven grandchildren.

CARRIE OTT
Editor, Designer
Carrie met Christ at an early age. All her life she has had a passion for words, and as a free-lance writer and designer, this passion doubles when it is words — seen, read, and grasped — that attempt to sketch a portrait of the mystery and wonder of God and His Word. Carrie identifies with Mechtild of Magdeburg, who said, "Of the heavenly things God has shown me, I can speak but a little word, no more than a honeybee can carry away on its foot from an overflowing jar." Carrie and her husband have three children and live in the Atlanta area.

To learn more about
Big Dream Ministries, Inc. and
The Amazing Collection,
visit their website at:

www.theamazingcollection.org

LEADER'S GUIDE

INTRODUCTION

Leading a group Bible study can be a challenging but incredibly rewarding experience. This Leader's Guide will provide help with the "challenging" part, as you trust God to produce the "incredibly rewarding" piece.

This guide is not designed to take you step-by-step through the individual studies. Instead, it will offer some general guidance and instruction in principles and techniques. Most of what you learn here will not be specific to *The Amazing Collection* but applicable to many kinds of group study. The one exception is Appendix B.

Each section of this Leader's Guide will deal with a single subject, making it easier for you to return to the guide for future help and reference.

Thank you for accepting the challenge and responsibility of leading your group! We pray God will make this a rewarding and profitable experience for you.

DISCUSSION: THE ESSENTIAL COMPONENT

The words *small-group Bible study* are almost synonymous with the term *discussion*. While there are very significant places and purposes for lecturing (one-way communication), for the most part a small group is not one of them. Therefore, discussion is an essential component of a successful small-group experience.

Discussion is the investigation of a subject or question by two or more people using verbal dialogue. Webster defines it as "consideration of a question in open debate; argument for the sake of arriving at truth or clearing up difficulties." Additionally, the word *discuss* and its synonyms mean "to discourse about so as to reach conclusions or to convince. Discuss also implies a sifting or examining, especially by presenting considerations pro and con."[1]

Small-group Bible studies will not always include debate or argument, but there *should* always be investigation, examination, and the reaching of at least tentative conclusions.

There are many benefits to discussion-style learning compared to lectures or even to interaction that is dominated by one person. Discussion:

- Keeps every member more involved in the learning process
- Allows for self-disclosure, enabling the participants to get to know each other better
- Helps crystallize the thinking of each group member by creating a venue in which topics can be investigated at deeper levels
- Creates a more informal atmosphere, which encourages a sense of relaxed learning
- Provides the potential of uncovering misconceptions and correcting misinformation
- Fosters more permanent learning and change because people tend to better remember what is said rather than what is thought
- Builds a sense of community as participants cooperate in their search for truth and understanding

While small-group Bible studies that foster healthy discussion will realize the above benefits, the depth of any group experience is greatly enhanced by an able leader. The leader plays an important role in helping each of these seven benefits become reality. For example, in order to keep every member more involved in the learning process, the leader will need to encourage those who tend to hide and manage those who tend to dominate. The other benefits require similar sensitivity by the leader. The remainder of this guide is intended to help the leader maximize these benefits for her small group.

But before we move on, one more issue should be addressed. While the leader is a crucial player in a small group, he or she should not become the person to whom all other participants address their remarks. One author has suggested that a discussion leader should strive to foster an "all-channel" network, rather than become the "hub" or center of a discussion wheel, as the following diagrams depict.

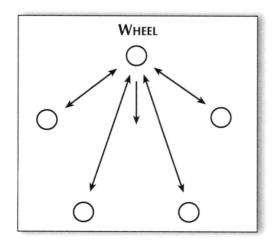

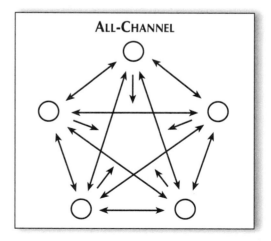

In a "wheel" network, all comments are directed toward one central leader, and he or she alone speaks to the group as a whole or to any one person.

By contrast, an "all-channel" network allows rapid communication without requiring clearance from a central gatekeeper; everyone is free to share thoughts that come to mind while they are still relevant to the topic at hand. Free exchange of questions and responses is thus encouraged.[2]

The leader's responsibility is to continually remember the need for "all-channel" communication.

LISTENING: THE LOST ART

You've probably heard it said that God gave us two ears and one mouth because He wanted us to listen twice as much as we talk. It would be difficult to prove that assumption, but the Bible *does* say:

> But everyone must be quick to hear, slow to speak. (James 1:19)

> He who gives an answer before he hears,
> It is folly and shame to him. (Proverbs 18:13)

Listening may be the most powerful tool of a successful small-group leader, but it is also possibly the most difficult trait to develop. Most people tend to talk more than listen, be more concerned about their interests than the interests of others, and listen impatiently, hoping the other person will finish quickly. True listening is a lost art, which a good small-group leader must recapture.

Listening is not just hearing. As reading is to seeing, listening is to hearing. By both reading and listening, we understand the real meaning of the words our senses "take in."

Consider the following ideas and use them to evaluate your own listening habits and skills. Then, decide which areas you could intentionally improve.

Listening Characteristics:
- It is active, not passive, and therefore sometimes tiring.

- It is other-centered, not self-centered, and therefore sometimes sacrificial.

- It is crucial, not peripheral, and therefore indispensable.

- It is difficult, not easy, and therefore often neglected.

- It is scarce, not common, and therefore greatly desirable.

Listening is not like:

- A chess game — planning your next verbal move while the other person is talking
- A trial — judging what is said or how it is said
- A 100-yard dash — thinking how quickly you can end the discussion

Listening is like:

- A sponge — absorbing as much as possible of what is being said and the feelings behind it
- A pair of binoculars — fixing attention on and bringing into clear focus what is being said

Kinds of Questions:

- Information — "What did you do today?"
- Opinion — "Why do you think that happened?"
- Feeling — "How do you feel about that?"

Kinds of Responses:

- Clarification — "I think what you're saying is . . ." This gets at the meaning of what was said.
- Observation — "I noticed that your voice dropped when . . ." This acknowledges the importance of nonverbal cues.
- Reflection — "You seem quite sad about . . ." This acknowledges the emotional component.
- Inquiry — "Tell me more about . . ." This seeks additional information and often gleans further insight.

While you are listening, consider silently praying for wisdom:

- "God, what are you doing in this person's heart right now?"
- "Father, help me to hear what she is really saying."
- "Eternal Counselor, what kind of response do you want me to make to what this person is saying?"

There will be times as a small-group leader when you will need to limit one member's input to allow for total group input. Your aim is not to encourage never-ending dialogue with one person, but to bring the most and the best out of each participant and the group as a whole, maximizing discussion, insight, and impact more fully than you may have thought possible.

Questions: The Mental Crowbars

Good questions can spell the difference between success and failure in a small-group setting. As you lead discussions of *The Amazing Collection*, the Learning for Life discussion questions at the beginning of each study will give you an excellent starting point. But there will be times when you will want to probe differently or more deeply. At such times, forming good questions will be incredibly important.

Some of these questions may be prepared ahead of time. Others will be developed as you go. Remember, every good question shares some common characteristics:

- Brief — short and uncluttered
- Applicable — relevant to the people's needs
- Simple — easily understood
- Interesting — capable of holding attention
- Conforming — based on the material being studied

As a leader you may ask launching, guiding, and application questions. The following material describes these three types of questions, giving examples of each.

Launching Questions:
- Initiate meaningful discussion on a subject
- May be prepared ahead of time
- Will determine to a large extent the direction your discussion will take
- Are general questions intended to stimulate discussion
- Must be based on the participants' previous study to enable quality contributions
  Examples:
  - "What did you discover in this passage about . . . ?"
  - "What impressed you most about how God . . . ?"
  - "What thoughts do you have about Moses after this study?"
  - "Why do you think God included this passage in the Bible?"
  - "How would you describe the holiness of God?"

Guiding Questions:
- Keep the discussion moving, drawing out the most important ideas and refocusing a wandering discussion
- May be prepared ahead of time as you anticipate the subjects that will be raised by the group

- May be crafted as the discussion is in high gear (This takes practice!)
- Take the participants beyond initial observations and more deeply into the meaning of the material

    Examples:
    - "Sally just mentioned the concept of obedience. How does that fit with what this passage seems to say?"
    - "Who else would like to comment on that?"
    - "We've said a lot of things about grace in our discussion. If you had to boil it down to a sentence, what would you say?"
    - "What we're discussing is interesting, but we've wandered from where we want to go. Can someone take us back to where we veered off the trail?"

Application Questions:
- Are supplied for you in *The Amazing Collection* workbooks
- May be developed based on your own knowledge of the group
- May be difficult to formulate but serve as the bridge from Bible study to daily living — from the head to the heart
- Do not always involve something concrete to do or to change
- Could include meditation, reflection, remembering, or simply waiting on God
- May be questions that will encourage the group to share their answers aloud or may suggest a more private response
- May be specific or general
- Must relate to the truth the group has just studied

    Examples:
    - "Write a prayer pouring out your heart to God in response to what He has been teaching you this week."
    - "Do you know someone who models well what we have just studied? How could you affirm that person this week?"
    - "What do you sense God is asking you to do in response to your study?"
    - "What do you see in this character's life that you would like to imitate? What would that look like? What is the first step?"

Crafting and asking questions are skills that can be developed and honed. After each group meeting, it might be useful to evaluate your questions. Did they lead the group where you sensed God wanted to lead? Which "as you go" guiding questions worked well or not so well? How did the group respond to the questions? Was there any confusion? Finally, make a point to review anything you learned about asking questions each week.

ROLES PEOPLE PLAY: THE ULTIMATE CHALLENGE

If being a small-group Bible study leader involved only facilitating discussion, learning to listen well, and forging meaningful questions, the challenge would be large enough. But add to that the fact that every person in your group will have different needs, temperaments and personalities, approaches to Bible study, reasons for being there, and levels of maturity, and the role of leadership becomes exponentially more challenging.

Professor Howard Hendricks of Dallas Theological Seminary describes in *How to Lead Small Group Bible Studies* some of the roles people play in group situations. You may find these helpful in evaluating your own group's dynamic.

Immature roles

The onlooker	Content to be a silent spectator. Only nods, smiles, and frowns. Other than this, he is a passenger instead of a crew member.
The monopolizer	Brother Chatty. Rambles roughshod over the rest of the conversation with his verbal dexterity. Tenaciously clings to his right to say what he thinks — even without thinking.
The belittler	This is Mr. Gloom. He minimizes the contributions of others. Usually has three good reasons why some opinion is wrong.
The wisecrack	Feels called to a ministry of humor. Mr. Cheerio spends his time as the group playboy. Indifferent to the subject at hand, he is always ready with a clever remark.
The hitchhiker	Never had an original thought in his life. Unwilling to commit himself. Sits on the sidelines until others reach a conclusion, then jumps on the bandwagon.
The pleader	Chronically afflicted with obsessions. Always pleading for some cause or action. Feels led to share this burden frequently. One-track mind.
The sulker	Lives with a resentful mood. The group won't always agree entirely with his views, so he sulks.

Mature roles

The proposer	Initiates ideas and action. Keeps things moving.
The encourager	Brings others into the discussion. Encourages others to contribute. Emphasizes the value of their suggestions and comments. Stimulates others to greater activity by approval and recognition.

The clarifier	Has the ability to step in when confusion, chaos, and conflict occur. He defines the problem concisely. Points out the issues clearly.
The analyzer	Examines the issues closely. Weighs suggestions carefully. Never accepts anything without first thinking it through.
The explorer	Always moving into new and different areas. Probes relentlessly. Never satisfied with the obvious or the traditional viewpoints.
The mediator	Promotes harmony between members — especially those who have trouble agreeing. Seeks to find conclusions acceptable to all.
The synthesizer	Able to put the pieces together from different ideas and viewpoints.[3]

No doubt you will see some of these roles typified by members of your small group. How you deal with members who play out the immature roles and how you encourage and utilize those who take on the mature ones will be an ongoing challenge. Ask the Spirit of God to give you sensitivity, creativity, and ability as you lead. Pray for wisdom to become your constant, ready resource.

Your Leadership: A Spiritual Endeavor

Before we move on, it is important to remember that beyond understanding and fostering discussion, learning to listen well, developing your skill in fashioning questions, and learning to lead different kinds of people, it is God who supplies the grace and strength that will carry you through the challenges of leadership.

This Leader's Guide has focused so far on you and your best efforts, but in truth you will accomplish absolutely nothing of eternal value unless the Spirit of God takes your faithful efforts and infuses them with His enabling power and grace.

For this reason, we encourage you to prepare and lead in complete humility, dependence, and trust, remembering these critical precepts:

I can do all things through Him who strengthens me. (Philippians 4:13)

"My grace is sufficient for you, for power is perfected in weakness." (2 Corinthians 12:9)

"I am the vine, you are the branches; he who abides in Me and I in him, he bears much fruit, for apart from Me you can do nothing." (John 15:5)

Finally, be strong in the Lord and in the strength of His might. Put on the full armor of God, so that you will be able to stand firm against the schemes of the devil. (Ephesians 6:10-11)

Our prayer for you is that of Paul's prayers for the Ephesians:

> That the God of our Lord Jesus Christ, the Father of glory, may give to you a spirit of wisdom and of revelation in the knowledge of Him. I pray that the eyes of your heart may be enlightened, so that you will know what is the hope of His calling, what are the riches of the glory of His inheritance in the saints, and what is the surpassing greatness of His power toward us who believe. These are in accordance with the working of the strength of His might. . . . [And] that He would grant you, according to the riches of His glory, to be strengthened with power through His Spirit in the inner man, so that Christ may dwell in your hearts through faith; and that you, being rooted and grounded in love, may be able to comprehend with all the saints what is the breadth and length and height and depth, and to know the love of Christ which surpasses knowledge, that you may be filled up to all the fullness of God. Now to Him who is able to do far more abundantly beyond all that we ask or think, according to the power that works within us, to Him be the glory in the church and in Christ Jesus to all generations forever and ever. Amen. (Ephesians 1:17-19; 3:16-21)

APPENDIX A

THE EFFECTIVE DISCUSSION LEADER: A WORTHY GOAL

This section presents a model for the effective discussion leader (EDL). You may not demonstrate every characteristic listed, nor do you need to. Some of these things you will do very well; others you will do okay; still others may be a weak area for you. That is just fine. Consider this list simply an ideal to aim for. Our hope is that it will motivate you to grow as a small-group leader by revealing your areas of strength and highlighting your areas of weakness for which you may need help. God never said He could use only perfect people in ministry. In fact, your limitations in one or more of these areas may allow for others in the group to come alongside and complement you by contributing their strengths.

You may choose to use this list with a group of leaders to discuss your common ministries and responsibilities and share with each other challenges and successes you've experienced as leaders. Hearing others' thoughts about each of these characteristics might encourage you as you continue to grow.

What key characteristics make an effective discussion leader?

1. EDLs have a good grasp of the material to be discussed.
   - They have studied the material in advance.
   - They have a clear purpose for the meeting.
   - They have an introduction planned.
   - They have questions planned.
   - They have a tentative conclusion in mind.
   - They have examined their own life in relation to the truth of the study.
   - They seek to be diligent workers who accurately handle the word of truth (see 2 Timothy 2:15).

2. EDLs are skilled in organizing group thinking.
   - They know how to use questions.

- They can detect tangents and gently but firmly bring the discussion back on track.

3. EDLs are open-minded.
   - They express judgments in a conditional way.
   - They encourage consideration of all points of view.
   - They encourage open-mindedness on the part of all the members.
   - They are able to handle incorrect answers by inviting further questioning or discussion.

4. EDLs are active participants.
   - They talk frequently yet not excessively.
   - They are not defensive or sensitive to disagreement or criticism.

5. EDLs are facilitators.
   - They do not give dictatorial directions.
   - They encourage participation by all.
   - They encourage interaction among all members.
   - They are able to manage members who tend to dominate discussion.
   - They are able to stimulate and involve shy or reticent members in nonthreatening ways.

6. EDLs speak well.
   - They speak clearly.
   - They speak in a concise, pertinent way.
   - They are not tactless, chattering, offensive speakers.

7. EDLs have respect for and sensitivity to others.
   - They are empathetic.
   - They do not attack others.
   - They do not cause others to "lose face."
   - They are aware of how others are reacting.
   - They are patient.

8. EDLs are self-controlled.
   - They can remain impartial when necessary.

- They can express their feelings in a direct, yet nonaccusatory manner.

9. EDLs can assume different roles.
   - They can give encouragement.
   - They can give direction when necessary.
   - They can insert humor to break the tension when appropriate.
   - They can lead the group in prayer to seek wisdom.
   - They can give personal attention to needy members.

10. EDLs give credit to the group and its members.
    - They praise the group for insights and progress.
    - They stress teamwork.
    - They make all the members feel important.
    - They value others as their equals.
    - They "do nothing from selfishness or empty conceit" but regard others as more important than themselves (Philippians 2:3).

11. EDLs are authentically transparent.
    - They share personal illustrations.
    - They share personal weaknesses, frustrations, pressures, and failures without seeking undue personal attention.
    - They share personal feelings.
    - They share personal requests.
    - They plan ahead so all this can be done with taste and genuineness.

12. EDLs are enthusiastic.
    - They pour themselves into the subject and the discussion of it.
    - They allow the subject to be poured into them by God prior to the discussion.
    - They recognize that genuine enthusiasm is a powerful motivator for others.

13. EDLs are properly critical and evaluative of their leadership.
    - They constantly look for ways to improve.
    - They regularly seek feedback and advice.
    - They consistently evaluate the various aspects of their leadership role.

- They remember that evaluation is not comparing themselves with others but is seeking the Holy Spirit's input on possible improvement.

14. EDLs know that leadership is a spiritual endeavor.

   - They regularly admit to God that apart from Him they can do nothing (see John 15:5).

   - They confidently say "I can do all things" and then humbly add "through Him who strengthens me" (Philippians 4:13).

   - They never forget God's promise that "My grace is sufficient for you" (2 Corinthians 12:9).

APPENDIX B

Suggested Formats for *The Amazing Collection*

The Amazing Collection is intentionally flexible to accommodate a variety of teaching settings and calendars. It is possible to complete the study of all sixty-six books of the Bible in two years by teaching a book a week for thirty-three weeks each year (excluding summers and holidays).

Another option would be to go through the material in three years, teaching a book a week for twenty-two weeks each year, perhaps beginning in September and going through April. Also, for individuals, the program could be completed in approximately fifteen months, studying a book a week for sixty-six consecutive weeks.

There is flexibility in each individual session as well. Sessions might last an hour, in which the group watches the video (forty-five minutes) and allows fifteen minutes for discussion. Or, a 1.5-hour format could include the video, fifteen minutes for refreshments, fifteen for discussion, and fifteen for homework review. If time permits, two-hour sessions could include the video, refreshments, thirty minutes for discussion, and thirty for homework review.

Maybe you'll discover another format that suits your group to a tee. Feel free to use it!

APPENDIX C

SHARING THE GOSPEL

Leaders should be sensitive to the fact that some group members may have an interest in the Bible without having established a personal relationship with its central figure, Jesus Christ.

Sharing the gospel is quite easy for some people and more challenging for others. But if you sense that there are members in your group who would benefit from a clear explanation of salvation, by all means, offer one! There may even be "natural" openings during your course of study (at the end of a book or workbook or during your study of the Gospels or the book of Romans) when the gospel seems to "tell itself." In addition, the vast majority of discussion questions (Old and New Testament) contain a question that points directly to the person of Jesus Christ. These are "teachable moments." Don't miss them.

Several excellent tools exist that can help you walk an unbeliever through the basics of salvation. *The Four Spiritual Laws, Steps to Peace with God, My Heart — Christ's Home*, and *The Roman Road* are just a few. The leaders in your church may be able to provide you with one or more of them.

Although there are many excellent video testimonies throughout *The Amazing Collection*, it may be appropriate at some point to briefly share your own personal testimony with your group or with one or more of its members. It may help to think of your "story" in four parts: your life before Christ, how you came to know and understand your need for forgiveness and reconciliation with God, what Christ did on your behalf on the cross, and how your life is different today having accepted His atoning sacrifice on your behalf. This is your story! Pray for a sensitive heart, the right timing, and the right words to share it when the Holy Spirit leads you to do so.

It is our prayer that no one would complete *The Amazing Collection* without a personal, saving knowledge of our Savior, the Lord Jesus Christ.